Contents

PRE-CONCEIVED IDEAS
A Christian Perspective *of* IVF *and* Embryology

Credits

General Editors: Hugh Brown
and Kristine Gibbs.
Design concept: Mark Blackadder.
Photographs: The Image Bank.
Diagrams: Paul Hatty.
Typeset in Palatino and Helvetica.

Published on behalf of:
The CHURCH of SCOTLAND
BOARD of SOCIAL RESPONSIBILITY
47 Milton Road East, Edinburgh EH15 2SR
by SAINT ANDREW PRESS
121 George Street, Edinburgh EH2 4YN.

Copyright ©
The CHURCH of SCOTLAND
BOARD of SOCIAL RESPONSIBILITY 1996

British Library in Cataloguing Data
   A catalogue record for this book is
   available from the British Library.
   ISBN 0 86153 223 6

Printed and **bound** in Scotland by:
*f*m print limited, Edinburgh.

Introduction

One of the features of the later part of the twentieth century is that we are witnessing almost unprecedented advances in medical science. At the same time there is a very marked decline in awareness of the basic moral principles which have undergirded our society throughout the century. Not only are these principles largely unknown by many, but they have sometimes been deliberately side-lined.

It is important that Christians should not only state Biblical principles, but also show how they relate to current issues. Society cannot be civilised without a moral code.

This Study is about one of the most important areas of life. Even those who do not share the presuppositions of the Study Group will find great value in the practical issues which are discussed.

The Study Group who produced this Report are to be congratulated for the way in which, with Biblical and intellectual integrity, they face the issues raised by rapid advance of medical science.

Rev. William F Wallace
Convener
BOARD OF SOCIAL RESPONSIBILITY
June 1996

Preface

The ethical dilemmas posed by reproductive medicine are complex. The rapid advances which have been made in the field of human fertilisation and embryology have left in their wake many questions concerning the sanctity of life, personal identity, the structure of the family, the role of medicine, and justice in the allocation of limited resources.

This Report, which has been produced by the Board of Social Responsibility of the Church of Scotland, and which was presented to the General Assembly in 1996, opens up the questions raised by reproductive technology in an objective manner. It sets out the options which are available to childless couples, and indicates what medical, legal and ethical issues are involved in the different solutions to the problem of infertility.

The psalmist in exile asked: 'How shall we sing the Lord's song in a strange land?' (Psalm 137:4). That is a challenge which Christians face in all walks of life. The Report is an attempt to sing that song in the strange land of reproductive technology, and is offered to the Church in the hope that it will stimulate the reflection, questioning, and discussion which will enable us to discern the will of the Lord in a field where complex questions do not encourage simple answers. In the words of the Apostle Paul: 'Test everything. Hold on to the good. Avoid every kind of evil' (1 Thessalonians 5:21-22).

Rev. David Easton
Convener
STUDY GROUP ON HUMAN FERTILISATION AND EMBRYOLOGY,
June 1996

PRE-CONCEIVED IDEAS
A Christian Perspective of
IVF and Embryology

What has the CHURCH previously said?

Remit

In 1994 the Board of Social Responsibility set up a Study Group on Human Fertilisation and Embryology with the following remit:

> *To consider from a Christian perspective the history and recent developments of human fertilisation and embryology; to study and comment on the social, moral, and ethical position of such developments; to alert the Church to the issues; and to make recommendations. The Study Group is required to take particular cognisance of the Reports submitted by the Board to the General Assembly on Childlessness (1982) and Human Fertilisation and Embryology (1985).*

Previous Reports to the General Assembly

The General Assembly of 1982 expressed appreciation of the ecumenical Working Party on Childlessness, and commended it to the study of the Church.

The deliverances passed by the General Assembly of 1985 were:

- receive with interest the comments of the Board on the Report of the Committee of Inquiry into Human Fertilisation and Embryology (the

Warnock Report), regretting the failure of the Report to give adequate consideration to the moral questions raised by the medical solutions offered to couples facing the problems of infertility and childlessness;

- note the Board's acceptance of AIH (artificial insemination by husband) and in vitro fertilisation (IVF), and support the Board's rejection of AID (artificial insemination by anonymous donor), egg donation, embryo donation, and surrogacy, which are incompatible with the Christian concept of marriage;
- welcome the Warnock Report recommendation that counselling should be available to all infertile couples and third parties at any stage of treatment for infertility;
- reject all non-therapeutic embryo experimentation as being contrary to the Christian belief in the sanctity of life;
- commend to the Church the continuing study of the moral issues raised by the directions currently being taken by medical science in the area of human reproduction.

The position taken by the Church in the 1982 and 1985 Reports may be briefly summarised as follows:

- The fertilisation of the ovum of a wife by the sperm of her husband through artificial means is not open to moral objection. However, the donation of eggs or sperm by a third party is open to the objection that the procedure involves the intrusion of a third party into the marriage relationship.
- By the same token, IVF as a technique to relieve infertility within the marriage relationship raises no moral objection, but moral objections do arise in principle if donated eggs or sperm are used.
- Surrogacy should be made illegal.
- So far as embryo research is concerned, the 1985 Report called for a halt to all experimentation which was not for the benefit of the embryo.

We may note in passing that the Church, in allowing IVF within the marriage relationship while ruling out embryo research, was accepting the benefits of IVF while condemning the means used to achieve them.

Background to the Report

Prior to the advent of in vitro fertilisation (IVF), infertile couples received little more than sympathy and some basic advice on how to improve their prospects of having a child. What medical interventions were available were of a rudimentary sort. The alternative to childlessness for many couples lay in the relatively easy access to adoption. However, improved techniques of contraception, the growing acceptance by society of single parenthood, and the affects of the Abortion Act [1967], substantially eroded this option. The birth in the UK in 1978 of Louise Brown, the world's first 'test-tube baby', heralded the dawn of a new era in the field of reproductive medicine. The means of intervening in human life in its earliest stages was now possible. There can be no doubt that assisted reproduction has afforded the opportunity and privilege of biological parenthood to couples who hitherto had little or no hope of having their own children.

Now hardly a week passes without news of some fresh break-through. In 1994 the first baby resulting from micro-injection of sperm was born in France. The procedure involved inserting a single sperm into the mother's egg by injecting it through its surrounding envelope. This technique offers an alternative for couples with male infertility problems which avoids recourse to donated sperm. Sex selection techniques are also being developed which would allow parents, who wish to avoid passing on a sex-linked gene defect, to choose the sex of their child at the moment of fertilisation rather than be faced later on with the choice between abortion and the prospect of giving birth to a handicapped child. Other techniques are being developed to screen embryos fertilised in vitro for genes linked to a high risk of certain cancers which might cause death in adulthood. Research is seeking to develop a reliable method for freezing unfertilised eggs so that eggs might be stored in 'egg banks' until needed, just as sperm and fertilised embryos are now preserved. This would allow eggs to be collected from women, who through surgery or cancer might lose the ability to conceive normally, and be stored until they were ready to have children.

The profile given to these developments by the media has been high, sometimes sensational. The more bizarre achievements of reproductive technology – (as when in December 1993 a black South African woman, married to a white man but unable to produce eggs of her own, gave birth to a white baby in a Rome clinic after opting to have the eggs of a white donor fertilised by her husband's sperm because she believed that a white child would have a better future than one of mixed race) – have fuelled fears that Aldous Huxley's nightmare vision in *Brave New World* of a society peopled by 'made to order' humans might be uncomfortably close.

But public interest in reproductive medicine is also driven by other factors. The expectations which infertility treatment have created means that demand is bound to increase. At the same time, the high cost of such treatment at private clinics and its limited availability under the National Health Service (NHS), means that all who want it are unlikely to receive it.

Concerns are also being expressed about the implications of infertility treatment for the family as traditionally understood. There is the perception that what God has joined together (human sexuality, the marriage of man and woman, and procreation), reproductive technology may put asunder.

Infertility treatment has also raised questions about the role of medicine. The task of medicine, according to the Hippocratic tradition, which sits well with both the Christian notion of God's dominion over life and death and with the humanist understanding of basic human rights and duties, is to heal. In reproductive medicine, however, there is the concern that the principle of healing is being supplanted by that of manipulation. A shift has also taken place in our understanding of to whom the doctor is accountable. In the past, the doctor's commitment to the patient came first. Medical ethics were in the main concerned with issues arising from that relationship. But the deepening concern in society about the wider ramifications of medical practice has led to a growing need for the medical profession to take account of the public view on how new developments, particularly in the field of reproductive medicine, affect issues of human dignity, personal identity, the structure of the family, and justice in the allocation of limited resources.

Whatever misgivings we may have about the developments which have arisen from reproductive medicine, the boundaries of what is possible will continue to expand as the pace of medical research increases. However, the effects of expanding knowledge and ever more sophisticated medical technology can be controlled, though many countries place no legal restrictions on treatment or research. In Germany IVF is permitted, but only research which is for the benefit of the individual embryo is allowed. In Eire, Portugal, Norway, and the Australian states of Victoria and South Australia, embryo research has been banned. In the UK, the policy has been to allow treatment and research, subject to controls. First, the Royal College of Obstetricians and Gynaecologists set up a voluntary licensing authority. This was followed by the Interim-Licensing Authority which in turn has been superseded by the Human Fertilisation and Embryology Authority (HFEA) which was set up in 1991 following the passing of the Human Fertilisation and Embryology Act (hereafter the Act) by Parliament in 1990. The Authority has been given the task of regulating embryo research, the storage of sperm, eggs, and embryos, and the use made of donated eggs, sperm, and embryos produced outside the human body.

It is against this background that the Study Group have examined from a Christian perspective the issues raised by the rapid advances which have been made in the field of human fertilisation and embryology. The questions are complex and we did not always agree on the answers. We therefore felt it right to

' ... the boundaries of what is possible will continue to expand as the pace of medical research increases.'

state at the start what our aim in producing the Report has been and to say something about the context in which we have sought to understand our differences. The Report goes on to consider childlessness, the causes of infertility, the methods of infertility treatment, and related questions of embryo research and storage. There follows a survey of what services are offered to infertile couples by the National Health Service, and a section on the law and assisted reproduction. The Report then sets out some of the ethical and theological principles which should guide the Church in considering the issues raised by reproductive technology. In the light of these guidelines, the final section of the Report comments on a number of specific issues.

The APPROACH *adopted by the* STUDY GROUP

The advances made in the field of human fertilisation and embryology in recent years have raised difficult questions for research scientists, the medical profession, childless couples, lawyers, moral philosophers. They have also raised difficult questions for Christians who place particular store on the value of human life and on the respect due to the person. We believe that everyone is created in the image of God and is called in Christ to manifest that likeness. Each person is loved by God and is of supreme value. As such, each person, irrespective of who he or she is, enjoys equality of dignity and status with every other person before God and must be treated with appropriate respect.

Should the respect which Christians accord to persons be accorded to the human embryo, at all stages of its life, even from conception? This is an issue which has aroused considerable debate among all concerned. Differences of view exist. Some accord the human embryo no moral status at all. Others affirm that we should

'Each person is loved by God and is of supreme value ....'

'Should the respect which Christians accord to persons be accorded to the human embryo, at all stages of its life, even from conception?'

page 9

grant to the embryo, from conception, the same respect and rights which we would to a person, since from the start it embodies a person who is as much the object of God's supreme concern as the child or adult. Still others argue that it is not meaningful to speak of the embryo as a person, for, in its early stage, it is at best a human being at the pre-personal stage of its existence. Within this group, there is still a variety of opinion concerning when the human embryo does become a person worthy of full respect. Others, again, wish to respect the embryo from its earliest stage because of its uniqueness and potential, but believe that this respect is outweighed by other moral demands, such as the duty to help infertile couples, or to reduce the incidence of inherited diseases.

The Study Group considered at length the variety of opinions expressed. We wish unanimously to affirm the sanctity of the human embryo from the moment of its conception and to accord to the human embryo at all stages of its life the respect which we are called to accord to persons. We were not, however, able to agree on solutions to childlessness which were acceptable to all. We recognised that the differing views found among us were held with integrity. We therefore felt that, in the absence of agreement, it was proper to lift the burden of judgment from the Study Group and place it on the informed conscience of those responsible for the offering of treatment and of those considering treatment. To that end, we have aimed to open up the issues raised by reproductive technology in an objective manner, setting out the options which are available to childless couples, and indicating what practical and moral issues are involved in the various forms of infertility treatment.

Another difficulty we have faced is that of addressing more than one audience at once. The Report is in the first place addressed to the Church. We have therefore attempted to outline those ethical norms which should inform our response to questions raised by reproductive medicine. These norms are shaped by a Christian world view which is rooted in the revelation God has given us in Scripture and in Christ. It follows that discussion of such matters as IVF, Donor Insemination (DI), or surrogacy, will be informed by the Christian understanding of the nature of human life, sexuality, and the family, while recognising the inherent tensions for Christians of holding to ethical norms in a world of need.

Secondly, we also have in mind those who have not been able to have a child and the professionals who work in the field of infertility treatment. Here our concern is to help both patient and clinician, who may or may not profess the Christian faith, to think through the complex questions which reproductive technology poses, recognising that the practical solutions offered may sometimes be in tension with the ethical norms to which one or both parties hold. For the Christian, this is the tension of being in the world, yet not of the world.

Thirdly, we realise the importance of catching the ear of those in the public domain who draw up legislation, shape policies, and mould attitudes. Here we acknowledge that it is not always possible to achieve God's ideal in a society which does not acknowledge the Christian world view, and where public policy is at best a hard won consensus evolved from the competing interests of different groups. Often the best that we may hope to achieve in a pluralistic society is the feasible and not the ideal. Often the strategy must be to appeal to what common ground may exist between secular and Christian perceptions in the hope that from that base legislation and public policies and attitudes may be nudged closer to the divine ideal. The arguments used may appeal to reason and human experience, rather than to Scripture and theology. This should not be seen as compromising our Christian convictions, but rather as an attempt to achieve shifts in the thinking and practice of those who do not share our Christian convictions. We do not hesitate to declare our Christian convictions and do so where appropriate in this Report.

Misunderstanding and confusion can arise when no allowance

'... it is not always possible to achieve God's ideal in a society which does not acknowledge the Christian world view .... Often the best that we may hope to achieve in a pluralistic society is the feasible and not the ideal.'

is made for the fact that the Church has to address different audiences, and that there is a form of discourse which is appropriate to each. The ethical norms which we affirm as Christians will inform the pastoral counsel we give to people in particular situations. It will guide us as we contend in the public domain for policies which we feel will most closely correspond to the divine ideal. We should not, however, allow the relativities of the pastoral situation or the requirements of public policy to shape our ethical norms. To do so is to reduce Christian ethics to pastoral care or public policy. It is to lessen or minimise the ideal, and confuse things that differ.

In addressing the questions raised by reproductive technology, we have realised the need to speak more than one language, *'speaking the language of Zion in the believing community and at times in the public square, but also speaking a broader, neutral language that will seek to make some dent in the market place of bioethics thinking and practice'* (Dennis Hollinger).

The psalmist in exile faced the same challenge when he asked: 'How shall we sing the Lord's song in a strange land?' (Psalm 137:4) It is a challenge which Christians face at all times in all walks of life. If the words of the song and the tune sometimes vary, that is perhaps not surprising, given that we are asked to sing, first to one audience and then another, and in response to very different circumstances. The Report is an attempt to sing that song in the strange land of assisted reproductive technology.

CHILDLESSNESS

When a couple are planning to get married they will probably discuss whether or not they want to have children, how many they want, and how soon they will have them. They assume these are choices they can make. When after several attempts to get pregnant nothing happens, they are surprised. After further unsuccessful attempts they begin to worry, if not panic. What about all their expectations, hopes and desires?

These expectations are normal and natural. The desire to have children of our own is legitimate and childless couples must not be told otherwise. Yet many infertile couples are made to feel guilty for wanting something they cannot have. The driving force of the maternal instinct should not be underestimated, particularly when it is not satisfied. It is not easily pushed aside or forgotten. The woman is constantly reminded of her infertility. As she gets on with her normal life she will inevitably meet pregnant women and children. Then, her monthly period is a personal reminder that she has failed again to conceive. Continual disappointment may lead to despair and depression which on occasions may need medical treatment.

The Book of Proverbs tells us that 'hope deferred makes the heart sick' (13:12). The couple who have to live with the constant deferral of their hopes are subject to a great number of emotions, chief among them a feeling of being let down – by family and friends who often, without meaning to, say hurtful things; by the medical profession whose professional approach may seem uncaring; and by God who has denied them the blessing of children. There is also the feeling of inadequacy – 'I'm not fully a woman if I can't have children', or 'I'm not a real man if I can't father a child'. This feeling is made worse by the blame game – 'It's all your fault. You're the infertile one. If I had married someone

'The desire to have children of our own is legitimate and childless couples must not be told otherwise. Yet many infertile couples are made to feel guilty for wanting something they cannot have.'

else I could have had children'. Or the guilt game – 'It's all my fault. It's because of me that we can't have children'.

Feelings of being let down and of inadequacy may lead to a deep sense of insecurity in their relationships with their relations and friends, their spouse, and with God. This in turn can result in a feeling of isolation. In their isolation they develop 'tunnel vision'. To quote Proverbs again: 'A longing fulfilled is a tree of life' (13:12). As far as they are concerned, the solution to everything is to have a baby. The quest can become an obsession which gradually interferes with every area of their lives. People who only come into contact with the couple at intervals (like the family doctor, the gynaecologist, and the minister), may be unaware of how much the desire to have a baby has taken over their lives.

Although the wish to have children is normal and good, when the desire grows to the point where the couple say, 'We *must* have a child at any cost', then it is neither emotionally or spiritually healthy. There is a cost to be paid in the quest for a child (and it is not just financial) which the couple would do well to weigh up. They should ask themselves if the price may not be too heavy to pay. The toll in terms of time, financial outlay, physical discomfort, psychological stress, marital strain, the setting aside of moral principle for the sake of having a baby, and possible loss of faith, can be high, with no guarantee of success.

Should a childless couple reach the desperate or even obsessional stage (echoing Rachel's cry, 'Give me children or I'll die', Genesis 30:1), an irrational element can take over in their thinking. What makes a post menopausal women in her sixties want to have a baby? What makes a couple consider a surrogate mother? The parental instinct can be transformed from a God-given gift to help bring up children, into a relentless tyrant.

Of course, not all childless couples react in the above manner. Although most find childlessness extremely hard to cope with, they do avoid becoming obsessive or behaving irrationally. They suffer in silence and are misunderstood by others who conclude

'There is a cost to be paid in the quest for a child ... which the couple would do well to weigh up.'

that they have opted to remain childless in the pursuit of a career or financial gain. But some find that their childlessness becomes for them a doorway to a deeper relationship with God, and the means of strengthening their marriage, and of finding fulfilment in other areas of life.

Nevertheless, we should not judge those for whom having a child becomes a life-dominating obsession. Those who have experienced no difficulty in having children will never fully understand the depth of pain which childless couples may feel.

The MEDICAL CONTEXT

This section of the report provides background information to help in the understanding of these important issues. It describes the context of reproduction and the processes of fertilisation, implantation and differentiation; it outlines the clinical problems associated with defects in the reproductive process; it sets out, in lay terms, the treatments available for infertile couples; and it identifies some of the problems associated with infertility treatment.

Fertilisation, Early Human Development and Related Clinical Problems

Several events occurring in sequence are all necessary for the creation of a new human being.

Before a new life is fully established, three physical events must occur:

- the first is fertilisation, when the sperm and the egg unite to create a new, genetically unique, conceptus with the full potential to develop into a new human being.
- the second is implantation, when the new conceptus attaches itself to the wall of the uterus and derives sustenance from the mother.
- the third is differentiation, when some of the cells within the conceptus develop the distinctive features which indicate the formation of a new human body.

Unless all three events occur, the result will be reproductive failure. Most of the treatments to correct infertility are designed to promote fertilisation and this will be described first.

Fertilisation

Fertilisation is the process in which a sperm from the male and an egg (or oocyte) from the female unite to form a new conceptus. The sperm and the egg, which are called gametes, each contain only 23 chromosomes which is half the number of all other human cells. When they join together at fertilisation, the new conceptus (or

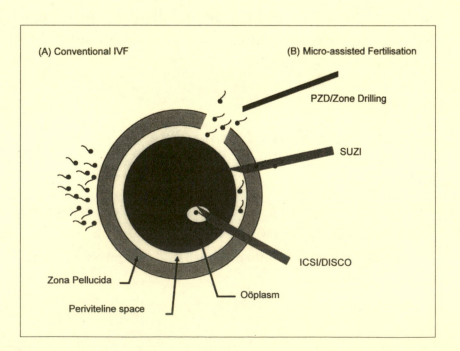

zygote) consists of 46 chromosomes carrying its own new, unique genetic structure.

The process of fertilisation is itself dependent upon a number of essential steps:

Sperm Production and Function

Sperm, which carry the male partner's genetic contribution, are produced in cells within the testis (the male sex gland) called germ cells. They are produced continuously in the adult male and in very large numbers; although only one sperm will ultimately fertilise the egg, many million are present in each ejaculate and are needed for fertility.

Sperm are shaped like tadpoles and are capable of forward swimming movements; they have to undergo a process called capacitation before they are able to enter the egg – these functions are needed for fertility.

If a sperm carrying a Y chromosome fertilises the egg, the conceptus will be a male; an X chromosome in the sperm leads to a female.

CLINICAL PROBLEMS

If a man is incapable of producing sperm (aspermia), the only treatment possible is donor insemination. If sperm have abnormalities of function (which is much more common), treatment may involve one of the following:

- intra uterine insemination with husband's semen (IUI);
- in vitro fertilisation (IVF);
- intra cytoplasmic sperm injection (ICSI).

These procedures are described below:

Oocyte (Egg) Availability

Eggs (oocytes) are all laid down in the ovary, the female sex gland, during fetal life. By the time of birth a female will already have lost many of her eggs and more will die before puberty. However, sufficient eggs survive until reproductive life in an immature form

'If a man is incapable of producing sperm … the only treatment possible is donor insemination.'

within structures called primordial follicles. These eggs carry the genetic contribution from the female to the new conceptus. All oocytes carry X chromosomes.

CLINICAL PROBLEMS

To be fertile, a woman must have eggs in her ovaries available for fertilisation. A small number of women of reproductive age have no eggs available for fertilisation either because of:

- genetic conditions causing ovarian absence or ovarian failure; or
- prior removal of the ovaries for medical reasons, such as ovarian tumours.

In addition, post menopausal women have no eggs available for fertilisation. In the above circumstances, the only treatment is egg (oocyte) donation (see page 29).

Oocyte Maturation and Ovulation

The female has a number of immature eggs in her ovaries within small follicles called primordial follicles. During the menstrual cycle, one egg is selected for maturation by the action of egg-stimulating hormones called gonadotrophins secreted by the anterior pituitary gland. Sometimes more than one egg is matured, leading to the possibility of multiple pregnancy. Over the first 14 days of the menstrual cycle, the fluid-filled follicle grows to about 18 millimetres and is visible to the naked eye; there is a maturing, but microscopic, egg within that follicle. At about day 14 of the menstrual cycle, the follicle ruptures, discharging the egg into the fimbrial end of the fallopian tube. This is called ovulation.

Ovulation is brought about by a large increase in the secretion of luteinising hormone, one of the gonadotrophins. The egg is viable for up to 24 hours after ovulation.

'The egg is viable for up to 24 hours after ovulation.'

CLINICAL PROBLEMS

If a woman fails to secrete gonadotrophins in sufficient amounts, or secretes them in an uncoordinated manner, egg maturation and ovulation will not occur. Ovulation failure is a common cause of infertility. Treatment is by one of the so-called fertility drugs used for ovulation induction (see page 24).

Transport of Sperm and Egg

For normal fertility, both sperm and egg must be able to move within the female genital tract. Sperm, placed at the top of the vagina during sexual intercourse, pass through the uterine cervix and the uterine cavity to reach the fallopian tube. Just before ovulation, the mucus in the cervix becomes receptive to the passage of sperm.

Sperm are viable for up to five days after intercourse. Fertilisation occurs at the distal end of the fallopian tube. The conceptus passes back along the fallopian tube to implant in the endometrium (the lining of the uterus).

'Sperm are viable for up to five days after intercourse.'

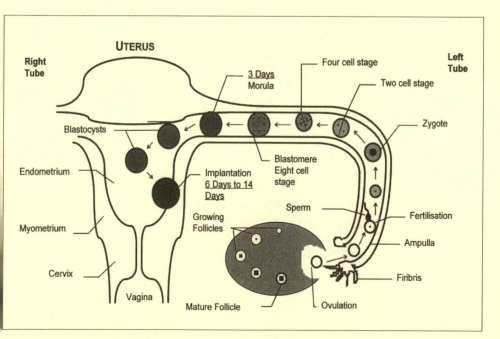

CLINICAL PROBLEMS

Any functional or physical obstruction to the transport of sperm or egg will lead to infertility. If the mucus in the cervix is hostile to sperm transport, this can be treated by intra uterine insemination.

Blockage of the fallopian tube, often secondary to infection, is a common cause of infertility. Surgical operations to relieve the problem have low success rates. However, it can be treated by in vitro fertilisation (IVF) (see page 27).

Penetration of Egg by Sperm

Many sperm bind to the surface of the egg, which is called the zona pellucida. One sperm penetrates the outer shell and enters the egg when fertilisation takes place.

CLINICAL PROBLEMS

If sperm function is inadequate, sperm penetration and fertilisation will not occur. Problems in sperm penetration may be treated by new methods such as intra cytoplasmic sperm injection (ICSI) (see page 16).

Implantation

After fertilisation, the new single cell conceptus is called a zygote (see diagram 1 on page 16). The conceptus begins to divide and pass back along the fallopian tube aided by fine cilia in the lining of the tube. If the lining of the tube has been damaged, the conceptus may be arrested in the tube leading to an ectopic pregnancy.

Normally, at the blastocyst stage the new pregnancy burrows into the lining of the endometrium. The endometrium has been prepared with rich oxygen and energy supplies as a result of actions of the female sex hormones, estrogen and progesterone, produced by the ovary during the course of the menstrual cycle.

Many fertilised eggs do not implant and are lost at the time of apparently normal menstrual bleeding. It is not possible to know exactly what proportion of all fertilised ova are lost but there is evidence to suggest that many unrecognised conceptions are lost in this way.

Differentiation

Initially, the cells of the conceptus are capable of becoming either the future placenta and membranes or precursors of the future embryo. If the cells of the early conceptus separate, two embryos may result as identical twins.

At about day 14 after fertilisation, some cells develop in a special way to be recognised as the 'primitive streak'. This is the first step in the process of differentiation into a recognisable human body. The conceptus now passes from the pre-embryonic to the embryonic stage.

CLINICAL PROBLEM

If differentiation does not occur, some placental tissue (or trophoblast) will develop within the uterus and subsequently be expelled as a miscarriage. This structure will be an empty sac with no recognisable 'soma' or body. It is termed a blighted ovum.

If abnormal differentiation occurs, a cystic tumour (called a hydatidiform mole) develops which, in some cases, may become a malignant trophoblastic tumour.

Some women suffer from reproductive failure because of recurrent spontaneous miscarriage. This is distinct from infertility and is a difficult condition to treat.

Prevalence and Investigation of Infertility

The Prevalence of Infertility

Infertility is a common condition affecting about 15 % of all couples [Templeton, 1995]. Infertility may be primary, when the couple have never had any children; or secondary, when there is an inability to conceive after having had a previous pregnancy, whether it resulted in the delivery of a child or a miscarriage. The prevalence of infertility appears to be stable in the Western world, but the demands for treatment have increased. This is due to social changes in society resulting in a dramatic reduction in the number of babies available for adoption, and also in an ever increasing expectation of successful treatment. It has been suggested [Templeton, 1995] that the demand for infertility services is unlikely to increase further, but it is possible that the development of new methods of infertility treatment, or improved results from current techniques, will encourage more couples to seek investigation and treatment.

Infertility is due to problems affecting the woman in 50 % of cases, or the male in 25 % of cases, although it is possible that there may be abnormalities affecting both partners. In the remaining 25 % of couples, there is no obvious cause for their infertility (unexplained infertility). Only in a small percentage of couples is infertility the result of factors related to their life-style or previous behaviour. Templeton states that currently in half of the couples who experience infertility, the problem will remain unresolved, in that 25 % of the total will not experience a pregnancy, and another 25 % will not achieve their desired family size.

The Investigation of Infertility

When pregnancy does not occur, partners should openly discuss their feelings with one another, so that they may support one another and make appropriate joint decisions. It is not normally necessary for a couple to seek medical advice until a year has past without pregnancy occurring. At this point, most couples will obtain medical advice from their General Practitioner about their failure to conceive. Discussion may identify causes of their infertility which are amenable to simple measures, such as timing of intercourse, and will also provide information about further investigations, some of which may be initiated by their GP.

Those who wish to commence fertility investigations and treatment should realise that the process results in anxiety and considerable emotional distress for many couples. Most will find it helpful to speak to close friends or others who have experienced infertility. There may be a local infertility support group to which they may relate. It is easy to proceed from simple to more complicated investigation and treatment without fully considering the implications in terms of time, money, the emotional upset, and whether the treatment is ethically acceptable. Couples should fully discuss the consequences at each stage before embarking on any treatment regime. They should also consider at which point it would be right to stop treatment and to consider alternatives, such as adoption or childlessness.

'Those who wish to commence fertility investigations and treatment should realise that the process results in anxiety and considerable emotional distress for many couples.'

Infertility Treatments

In response to the above clinical problems, a variety of treatments for infertility have been developed, with much scientific progress being made over the last two decades.

These treatments can be divided into:

- those which only involve the gametes (the cells carrying the genetic material) of the two partners;
- those involving the gametes or the uterus of a third party.

Methods using the Gametes of the two Partners

Ovulation Induction

When a woman is unable to ovulate because of abnormal gonadotrophin production, infertility will result (see page 18, above).

This clinical problem can be treated by methods of ovulation induction either by stimulating the mother's own gonadotrophins (endogenous production) or by giving her gonadotrophins from an external source (exogenous production).

(a) Stimulation of the woman's own gonadotrophins:
 (i) This can be done using drugs, the most common being Clomiphene which is successful in about 50 % of cases.

CLINICAL ISSUES

Clomiphene causes multiple pregnancy in about 8 per cent of cases, the great majority of these being twins; monitoring of possible over-stimulation is not usually carried out and the drug is used in general gynaecology and infertility clinics.

 (ii) Gonadotrophin releasing hormone (Gn Rh) –
 This is a new and very specialised treatment given only to selected cases in specialist centres. It is given by continuous infusion, but seeks to replicate normal gonadotrophin production by the patient.

CLINICAL ISSUES

This is an expensive treatment requiring highly specialised services and is infrequently used for ovulation induction.

(iii) Bromocriptine –

In a special condition called hyperprolactinaemia (high levels of the hormone prolactin), successful ovulation can be induced with the drug bromocriptine.

CLINICAL ISSUES

This drug is only suitable for a very small number of women with ovulation failure but works well in appropriate cases.

(b) Replacement of the woman's own gonadotrophins:

It is now possible to give gonadotrophins by injection to a woman to stimulate her ovaries to ovulate. By using these externally prepared (exogenous) gonadotrophins, several eggs may be matured during one cycle with the risk of multiple pregnancy (twins, triplets, quads, *etc*). To prevent over stimulation of the ovaries, careful monitoring of the woman is necessary using hormone measurements and ultrasound scans. Ovulation induction using gonadotrophins is a very successful treatment in properly selected cases.

CLINICAL ISSUES

- Treatment with gonadotrophins is very expensive because of the high cost of the drugs and the need for close monitoring in specialist centres.
- High order multiple pregnancy (especially quads and upwards) carries a high risk of premature (pre-term) birth and childhood handicap.
- The increased numbers of pre-term births from infertility treatment has put great pressure on special and intensive care nurseries.
- Because of the problems of high order multiple pregnancy the procedure called selective reduction is sometimes carried out (see pages 73 and 74).
- Ovulation induction with gonadotrophins is used to stimulate multiple egg development prior to in vitro fertilisation (IVF) (see next section).

In Vitro Fertilisation (IVF) and Gamete Intra-Fallopian Transfer (GIFT)

(a) In Vitro Fertilisation:

When fertilisation is not possible due to a blockage in the fallopian tube, IVF can be used to overcome the problem (see pages 16 and 19 above).

IVF was the method first used successfully by Edwards and Steptoe in 1978 and has revolutionised assisted reproduction. In IVF, eggs are collected from the follicles in the woman's ovary, immediately prior to ovulation. They are collected through a fine needle passed into the ovary using an ultrasonically directed probe in the vagina. Prior to IVF, the ovaries are stimulated by gonadotrophins to produce several eggs. These are then mixed with the sperm in the laboratory and incubated until fertilisation and the new conceptuses have divided to the 4 or 8 cell stage. The embryo is put into the uterus through a fine catheter.

In some units, IVF leads to pregnancy occurring in about 20 % of treatment cycles [Hull, 1994]. The success of IVF falls off when the woman is over 40 years of age. To increase the chance of successful pregnancy, more than one fertilised egg is usually transferred to the uterus, subject to a legal maximum of three.

New research has shown IVF to be successful also in the treatment of infertility due to endometriosis, some male infertility and some cases of unexplained infertility.

(b) Gamete Intrafallopian Transfer (GIFT):

An alternative treatment is GIFT, which is usually used for unexplained infertility. In this treatment the eggs and sperm are mixed and immediately replaced in a healthy fallopian tube.

GIFT does not generate spare embryos. In women with

'… IVF leads to pregnancy occurring in about 20 % of treatment cycles …. The success of IVF falls off when the woman is over 40 years of age.'

healthy tubes and men with favourable sperm, GIFT has pregnancy rates of about 35 % per treatment cycle.

CLINICAL ISSUES

- IVF (and to a lesser extent GIFT) is a relatively expensive treatment; costs range from £1000–£3000 per cycle of treatment. Some health boards are unwilling to purchase this treatment for NHS patients (see pages 42-43).
- IVF may generate spare embryos if more than three eggs are fertilised in one cycle of treatment.
- Spare embryos can be frozen and stored, raising legal and ethical issues.
- Units carrying out IVF are subject to the regulations of the HFEA which include regular inspection of premises, staff and records.
- Current evidence does not suggest any increase in fetal abnormality rate from IVF or GIFT treatments.

Treatment of Male Infertility

Until recently, treatment of infertility due to defects in the male was very unsuccessful. As noted above, some cases of infertility can be treated successfully using in vitro fertilisation. This approach will work in some cases where there are problems of sperm motility. IVF serves to bring the sperm and egg together by artificial means.

Other approaches to the treatment of male infertility are intra uterine insemination (IUI) and intra cytoplasmic sperm injection (ICSI).

(a) Intrauterine insemination (IUI):

The principle behind this treatment is to introduce sperm high into the uterus as close as possible to the oocyte. Claims have been made for success with this treatment but review of the literature throws doubt upon its effectiveness [Hull, 1994].

(b) Intracytoplasmic Sperm Injection (ICSI):

Infertility will result if sperm, due to defects in function, cannot penetrate the external surface of the egg. A new approach is to insert a sperm directly into the cytoplasm of the egg (or ooplasm) using micro-manipulation. This technique is called intra cytoplasmic sperm injection (ICSI).

ICSI has only recently been developed, but early reports suggest that it may be a successful form of treatment in cases where there are very few sperm in the ejaculate, provided that one viable sperm can be isolated. ICSI may also be an appropriate treatment if IVF is unsuccessful.

CLINICAL ISSUES
- IUI has the advantage of being simple, inexpensive and relatively free of ethical controversy.
- ICSI requires specialist equipment and staff and is expensive.
- Early experience of ICSI has not suggested increased risk of fetal abnormality.

Methods using Gametes of a Third Party

Donor insemination (DI) – formerly called artificial insemination by Donor (AID)

Until recently, treatment of male infertility was very ineffective. The options facing a couple with male infertility were adoption or donor insemination.

In donor insemination, sperm from a third party (the donor) are inserted into the vagina during the pre-ovulatory phase of the menstrual cycle. Donors have to be screened for human immuno-deficiency virus (HIV) and the sperm frozen and stored for three months before use to ensure that HIV infection is not present in the sperm sample. Information about donors is recorded: identifying information (*ie* name, address, *etc*) is kept strictly confidential, but non-identifying information (height, hair colour, *etc*) can be released to the recipient.

CLINICAL ISSUES

- Successful conceptions with DI are less than with natural intercourse.
- DI requires careful organisation to maintain confidentiality.
- A single donor's sperm must not be used to father more than ten children (see HFEA Code of Practice).
- An important question is what to tell children conceived by DI of their genetic origins.

Oocyte Donation

There are a small number of women who are unable to generate their own oocytes. In such cases, pregnancy can be achieved using oocyte donation.

Oocyte donation uses the methods of in vitro fertilisation, except that the egg comes from a donor and not from the woman herself. Eggs may be donated by:

(i) women undergoing assisted reproduction who donate extra oocytes;

(ii) women undergoing surgery, such as sterilisation;

(iii) Altruistic donors who may or may not be relatives of the recipient.

The endometrium of the recipient must be prepared to synchronise with the cycle of the donor by the use of hormone preparations. Oocyte donation has a rate of successful pregnancy similar to IVF.

CLINICAL ISSUES

- What guidance should there be about the selection of egg donors?
- Should egg donation be available for post-menopausal women?
- Is it ethical in infertility treatment to use eggs from cadavers or from fetal ovarian tissue? The present position is that the HFEA approves the use of ovarian tissue from live donors for infertility treatment. The use of ovarian tissue from cadavers has not been approved as yet, though the Authority sees no objection in principle. The use of fetal ovarian tissue is not allowed by law.

'Donor insemination requires careful organisation to maintain confidentiality.'

'The use of fetal ovarian tissue is not allowed by law.'

page 29

EMBRYO RESEARCH
and STORAGE

Years of embryo research have been needed to bring assisted reproduction to its present stage of development. Under the terms of the Act, Parliament decided that research be permitted on the pre-implantation embryo under strict controls. Under the Act –

' ... it is illegal to keep a developing embryo beyond 14 days.'

(a) it is illegal to keep a developing embryo beyond 14 days. The phase of the pre-implantation embryo lasts for 14 days from the moment of fertilisation until the development of the primitive streak, which occurs when the cells which are to form the fetus separate from the cells which will form the placenta and umbilical cord;

(b) all research on human pre-implantation embryos must be licensed by the HFEA which must be satisfied that the research is necessary or desirable for at least one of the following reasons:

- to promote advances in the treatment of infertility;
- to increase knowledge about the causes of congenital disease;
- to increase knowledge about the causes of miscarriage;
- to develop more effective techniques of contraception;
- to develop methods for detecting the presence of gene or chromosome abnormalities in embryos before implantation;

(b) it is illegal to:

- place a human embryo in an animal;
- replace the nucleus of a cell of an embryo with a nucleus taken from elsewhere;
- alter the genetic structure of any cell while it forms part of an embryo;
- produce identical individual by genetic replacement;

(d) in addition, all proposed research projects have to be approved by a properly constituted local ethics committee and all projects are refereed by at least two independent experts. The HFEA have to be satisfied that the use of human pre-implantation embryos is essential for the research and that it could not be done in animal tissue.

In its 1994 annual report, the HFEA listed 39 licensed research projects in the following areas:

congenital diseases	1
genetic abnormalities	8
infertility problems	28
miscarriage	2

Some projects fell within more than one category. In their 1995 Report, only 24 research projects were recorded as being currently licensed.

Issues

In considering their attitudes to research on human pre-implantation embryos, the Study Group identified four central issues as particularly relevant:

- The potential benefit from the research.
- General concerns about the effects of the research.
- The status of the pre-implantation embryo.
- The supply of pre-implantation embryos for research.

Potential Benefits From Research
on the Pre-Implantation Embryo

There are a number of benefits from embryo research, the most important being as follows:

(a) Treatment of infertility:

The methods of assisted reproduction which are now being widely used to relieve the complaint of infertility (such as IVF) came about only because of previous research which used pre-implantation embryos. Much of the currently approved research using human pre-implantation embryos is designed to improve the success rates of the new methods of treatment thereby reducing the physical, emotional, and financial burdens on the prospective parents.

(b) Prevention of inherited disease:

It is estimated that about 21,000 children are born each year with significant genetic defects – such as cystic fibrosis, haemophilia, muscular dystrophy, Huntington's chorea and many more [HFEA Annual Report, 1994]. It is now possible that research, using the pre-implantation embryo, will develop new methods for preventing such inherited diseases. This would be done by sampling a cell from the pre-implantation embryo to test it for the defective gene; only embryos free from the disease would be re-implanted into the mother, with the embryos carrying the affected gene being allowed to die.

(c) Other possible benefits:

It has been argued that over-population is one of the greatest threats to the planet and the human race; research using the pre-implantation embryo could lead to new, improved methods of contraception. Miscarriage is a source of great anguish to parents, particularly when it occurs on a recurrent basis; research on the pre-implantation embryo could improve understanding of why such miscarriages occur.

In its report in 1994 from the USA, the National Institutes of Health Human Embryo Research Panel concluded that the promise of human benefit from research using human embryos was significant [*Ethics & Medicine*, 1995, 11.1]. This view is supported by the great majority of scientific opinion including the Royal College of Obstetricians and Gynaecologists in the UK.

General Concerns about the Effects of Embryo Research

Despite the potential benefits of embryo research, many deep concerns are felt by the public about its possible consequences. Some of the most important of these concerns are summarised below.

(a) Risks to children born after pre-implantation diagnosis:
 In the process of pre-implantation diagnosis, one cell is removed from the developing embryo for diagnostic purposes. At present, it seems that such a manoeuvre does not threaten the viability of the embryo because the remaining cells are able to divide and replace the removed cell. Nevertheless, it will only become fully evident that the procedure is free from adverse effect after substantial experience has been gained. Despite the good intentions of pre-implantation diagnosis, concerns about its safety will persist until a substantial amount of practical experience has been gained, and this will take many years to accumulate.

(b) Potentially adverse social effects:
 The new methods of assisted reproduction bring nearer the possibility of research involving cloning and gene manipulation. The unscrupulous use of such experiments have been banned

by Parliament and it has established the HFEA to ensure this is enforced rigorously.

Under the heading of 'genetic diagnosis', the possibility of using the new technology in eugenic programmes causes the public genuine concern. An extension of eugenics could be the rejection of individuals with imperfect genetic constitutions in pursuit of the 'perfect' child. Such attitudes are contrary to the view of all people being equal in God's sight and threaten the reproductive rights and freedoms of individual people. For example, laws have been passed in China which aim to reduce the perceived burden of disability to Chinese society. The law makes compulsory pre-marital examination for serious genetic disease, pre-natal testing for genetic defects and termination if a serious genetic disease is diagnosed [*Lancet*, 1995].

Status of the Pre-Implantation Embryo

A major factor (if not *the* major factor) in determining attitudes to embryo research, is the view taken of the status of the pre-implantation embryo. The Study Group considered two broad attitudes to this key question:

(a) The first is that the pre-implantation embryo is fully human from the moment of conception with moral and legal rights equal to those of a fetus and a new-born child. This view is consistent with that taken by the Church of Scotland in 1985: 'From its belief in the inviolability of the human fetus, the Board rejects the production of spare embryos or research on embryos, within any time period.'

(b) The second view is that during its pre-implantation stage, the conceptus has special status and the potential of becoming a human, but that this potential is not realised until the primitive streak (the first sign of a separate definitive human body) starts to form. Prior to this event, the conceptus has no sentience or separate body. In natural reproduction, large numbers of pre-implantation embryos die without the woman ever being aware that she has conceived. The view taken by the Warnock Committee (1984) was that the pre-implantation embryo had not achieved the same moral or legal status of the fully formed fetus. This was also accepted, *de facto*, by Parliament in the Human Fertilisation and Embryology Act (1990).

Distinction between these two points of view and their ethical implications is of crucial importance (see page 55).

Supply of Pre-Implantation Embryos used for Research

Notwithstanding the attitudes which are adopted towards the ethical acceptability of embryo research, the Study Group recognised that such research was now taking place within the terms of the Act and that it was necessary to consider the supply of pre-implantation embryos used for such work. The following were recognised as important issues:

(a) Creation of 'spare' embryos:

In most patients undergoing IVF, drugs are used to yield several mature eggs in a single menstrual cycle. These are collected by aspirating the eggs from the woman's ovaries through a fine needle guided to the correct place under ultrasound control. This process of 'superovulation' has the advantage of increasing the chances of fertilisation and establishing a successful pregnancy. In any one cycle, only two or a maximum of three fertilised eggs are replaced although more early embryos may have been produced as a result of the 'superovulation'.

In the majority of treatment cycles any 'spare' embryos which are not used in the first treatment cycle are stored and can be replaced in subsequent treatment cycles. If, however, the woman successfully achieves a pregnancy, these spare embryos may not be needed for therapy and be available for research.

(b) Informed consent:

There has been discussion about who have the rights over and the responsibilities for spare embryos. Although the treatment centres have important responsibilities, it is also clear that the donating couple have a major interest in the fate of any 'spare' pre-implantation embryo. It is an important basic principle that donors of gametes or embryos must give fully informed consent for any proposed research.

(c) Purchase or sale of embryos:

As there is a shortage of pre-implantation embryos for research, a situation which is likely to persist, there may well be the temptation for researchers to offer payment or other inducements to donors of embryos to allow their spare embryos to be used for research. A distinction can be drawn between payment and reasonable compensation to cover expenses, such as travel to meet with researchers and give informed consent.

(d) Pressure on donor couples to agree to research:

Couples who are infertile and are seeking to have assisted reproduction are often desperate for success and are willing to agree to anything which will improve their cause. There is clear temptation to over-enthusiastic researchers to offer advantages, such as reduction of cost or waiting list time, to couples who give written or unwritten consent to allow their spare embryos to be used for research. It is even possible that couples might be given the impression that their inclusion on a treatment programme would depend upon their attitude to their spare embryos being used for research.

'... donors of gametes or embryos must give fully informed consent for any proposed research.'

'... there may well be the temptation for researchers to offer payment or other inducements to donors of embryos to allow their spare embryos to be used for research.'

(e) The generation of embryos specifically
    for research purposes:

It is possible to generate pre-implementation embryos specifically for the purpose of carrying out research. For example, it is possible to collect an egg from a woman undergoing sterilisation and to fertilise the egg using donor sperm. Alternative sources of eggs for research could be from the ovaries of an aborted fetus, or from women who have recently died.

Following public consultation, the HFEA has concluded that the use of ovarian tissue from all three sources to produce embryos is acceptable, subject to existing controls and provided that informed consent is obtained from the live donor, or from the woman undergoing abortion, or had been obtained from the woman who had subsequently died.

Views of the Study Group

The Study Group members considered these four major causes of concern and the following summarises their views:

Potential Benefits From Embryo Research

The Study Group recognised the force of the arguments supporting the potential benefits from research on the pre-implantation embryo. Even those members who, after careful consideration, rejected embryo research on moral principle, felt 'the strong tug between principle and compassion'.

In trying to balance the benefits of research against the status of the embryo, some felt greater sympathy for research on genetic disease, congenital abnormality and miscarriage than for contraception and infertility. Others found it more difficult to distinguish between the different reasons for the research.

All of the members felt strongly that all research using human pre-implantation embryos must be scientifically valid and ethically

'Even those who rejected embryo research on moral principle, felt "the strong tug between principle and compassion".'

approved and carried out in established centres. They welcomed strongly the important role of the HFEA in ensuring that good practice was observed.

Concerns About the Effects of Embryo Research

All members of the Study Group felt that the general concerns of the public about embryo research were valid and that the public required accurate and understandable information about the issues involved. They stressed the importance of ongoing work to monitor the health and psychological well-being of the children produced by all forms of assisted reproduction. In particular, it was essential to monitor potential adverse effects from pre-implantation biopsy techniques.

The UK legislation, making illegal certain forms of research such as cloning and placing human cells in an animal, was welcomed.

The potential problem of eugenic manipulation is of major importance and goes beyond embryo research. The Study Group agreed in the strongest terms, that attitudes which discriminated against individuals on any grounds should be rejected spiritually, morally and legally, as being against the fundamental principle that all people are equal in God's sight.

The Status of the Pre-Implantation Embryo

This was the key issue of discussion. It will be discussed fully below (pages 55-60).

Supply of Pre-Implantation Embryos for Research

The Study Group, recognising that research on pre-implantation embryos is legal under the terms of the Act, and that the generation of 'spare' embryos is an inevitable consequence of current techniques of assisted reproduction, took the view that the following safeguards are essential for their use in research:

- The fully informed consent of the donating couple should be obtained for any proposed research.
- The purchase or sale of embryos for research should be prohibited.
- Direct or indirect pressure should not be brought to bear upon couples to agree to their embryos being used for research.
- Embryos should not be generated for the sole purpose of carrying out research.

Embryo Storage

Background

The HFEA Code of Practice lays down that no more than three embryos can be replaced in an IVF treatment cycle. Because IVF commonly produces more than the maximum three eggs, these may be fertilised, frozen and stored as pre-implantation embryos. The options for such stored pre-implantation embryos are as follows:

(i)   Use by the parents themselves in a subsequent treatment cycle should the first treatment cycle be unsuccessful.

(ii)   Use by the parents themselves after a substantial period of time to achieve a further pregnancy in the event of the first treatment cycle being successful.

(iii)   Donation of the pre-implantation embryo to another couple seeking to achieve a pregnancy.

(iv)   Use of the pre-implantation embryo for research after fully informed consent has been given by the donating couple.

(v)   Destruction of the spare embryo.

In treatment centres, where freezing facilities do not exist, spare embryos will be destroyed without storage unless they are donated to another couple or used for research. The Act stipulated

'The HFEA Code of Practice lays down that no more than three embryos can be replaced in an IVF treatment cycle.'

that the maximum time period for storage would be five years, beginning with those embryos in storage at 1st August 1991, when the HFE took up its powers. However, in December 1995 the HFEA recommended an increase of the maximum storage time to ten years.

Issues and Views of the Study Group

Alternatives to Embryo Storage

For some, the concept of embryo storage and the potential of destruction raised ethical difficulties because of their view that the embryo, at all stages, had the status of a human. For them, the optimum choice for individuals seeking IVF would be treatment using unstimulated cycles. In this way, the production of 'spare' embryos would be obviated and the need for destruction would be overcome. Treatment using unstimulated cycles has been pioneered in one centre and the Study Group recommend that this option should be more readily available to those who have ethical concerns about the fate of 'spare' embryos.

A further alternative to embryo storage would be egg storage which would overcome the ethical difficulty of 'spare' embryos. At present, the option of egg storage is not available because of technical difficulties with this method. The Study Group recommends further research to overcome this problem.

The Clinical Outcome following re-implantation of Frozen Embryos

'The information currently available has not substantiated concerns that freezing might harm human embryos.'

The information currently available has not substantiated concerns that freezing might harm human embryos. At present, there is no biological reason why embryos could not be stored indefinitely. However, only substantial experience will show whether or not prolonged freezing has a detrimental effect on stored embryos. The Study Group regard continuing monitoring of this as being of the highest importance.

Informed Consent of the Parents

The issues surrounding embryo storage are complex. Under the HFEA Code of Practice, couples must be counselled about the fate of any spare embryos prior to treatment being carried out. They are not obliged to agree to storage, but, if they do so, they must give written agreement to the duration of that storage. If the couple wish that the embryos be stored, whether for their own use, for donation, or research, consent can be varied or withdrawn.

The Study Group wishes to emphasise the importance of full, effective and sympathetic counselling to couples who are making very difficult decisions at a vulnerable time in their lives.

Ten Year Storage Limit

Where the consent form does not specify a shorter storage period, the maximum period imposed by law applies and at the end of that period, embryos must be allowed to perish.

The Study Group recognises both the impracticability and the undesirability of the right to indefinite storage. For example, after the end of the reproductive life-span of the mother or following her death, the case for the continuing storage of the embryo would be difficult to sustain.

However, the Study Group remains concerned about the imposition of an arbitrary maximum, even now that the HFEA has recommended it be extended from five to ten years. There may be circumstances when a longer period might be appropriate, *eg* where embryos are stored because of cancer in one or other partner, and the opportunity to create new embryos does not exist. In that situation, the genetic parents may well feel that the embryo is 'theirs', and that they have a right to be consulted about its fate.

Disposal of the Embryo

The decision to destroy an embryo may be an important moment in the lives of the parents concerned, no matter how small the embryo may be. Some parents may want to have the embryo disposed of with prayer and this wish should be respected. The Study Group wish to draw this potential need to the attention of the Church and to Ministers and ask them to respond sympathetically. Hospital Chaplains may be well placed to play a supportive role in these circumstances

COST *and* ACCESS *to* TREATMENT

Services within the National Health Service are provided at three Levels, and these, broadly speaking, are categorised as follows:

Level I

These are provided largely within the relevant Health Board Area, and consist of initial assessment, support and advice, generally at the level of the General Practitioner.

Level II

These diagnostic and initial treatment services are provided at Community Clinics, and hospital clinics (Local District and General Hospitals, some of which may have their own specialist infertility clinic), and utilise treatments which can include ovulation induction.

Level III

These services are provided by specialist centres within a limited number of hospitals (primarily in Aberdeen, Dundee, Edinburgh and Glasgow). The services of these clinics are purchased by several Health Boards, after assessment of potential requirement of such infertility services.

In a report published by the Scottish Office Home and Health Department in 1993, entitled 'Infertility Services in Scotland', the NHS in Scotland Management Executive did not require that Level III services for the treatment of infertility be provided free of charge by the NHS. They did, however, draw up guidelines for eligibility criteria for acceptance into a programme of infertility treatment, but it was left to the individual Health Boards to decide on the pattern and extent of infertility services which they wished to purchase, in the light of assessment of local community needs.

What follows represents the situation when this Report was being compiled. The situation is fluid, with the Health Boards continually reviewing the requirement for provision of infertility treatment, the eligibility criteria for acceptance of patients, the nature of the treatment to be recommended, and the cost effectiveness of existing and new treatments, relative to their success rates.

There are 15 Health Boards in Scotland, and all of these were approached for information with respect to provision of services; whether or not patients were expected to contribute to the cost of infertility treatment; and what proportion of each Health Board budget was spent on provision of these services.

The proportion of the cost of Level I and II service provision with respect to infertile patients is impossible to calculate, as it is not specifically administered under such a heading; and even at Level III, it is not always possible to give an accurate figure. The information provided by the Health Boards with respect to the proportion of their total budgets allocated to alleviation of infertility is therefore an estimated value.

Of the 15 Area Health Boards approached, a response was received from 14. Included in these responses was a reference to 'The Report of the Third National Survey of NHS Funding of Infertility Services', commissioned by the National Infertility Awareness Campaign, prepared by the College of Health, and published in July 1995. This contained information for the UK, including data from eleven of the 15 Scottish Health Boards

Access to treatment

Access to Level III infertility services are provided at present by most Health Boards. Treatment in the private sector is also available.

For those Boards which voluntarily supplied the information, it appears that, although the Patient Charter Guarantee does not apply in terms of the waiting times for Level III infertility treatment, increased financial provision is being made to try to reduce these waiting times.

Cost of treatment

In general, most of the Health Boards which provide Level III infertility services provide these in the form of IVF and do not ask for financial contributions from the patients; however, for IVF, they will normally only provide three cycles of treatment, so that a greater number of patients may be treated within the financial constraints set for such treatment. In addition, other forms of assisted conception may not be available from NHS funding. In terms of the cost to the Health Boards, those who were able to provide the Study Group with data indicated that, although the costs of provision of Level III infertility services represented between 0.03–1.0 % of their total Area Health Board budget, this figure was normally between 0.03 and 0.1 %.

Attitudes to the use of modern technology for the relief of infertility must take into account the cost, both in terms of money, and the time commitment of highly skilled medical, nursing, and technical personnel. Therefore, it raises questions of justice in the allocation of resources.

Each course of IVF currently costs a couple (or the NHS) from

£1000 to £3000, and carries a failure rate of at least 80 %. Even with several cycles of treatment there is no guarantee of success. Clearly, the cost is out of the reach of many childless couples in the UK, let alone those in poorer parts of the world. In the NHS, such expenditure has to be considered alongside many other needs which are currently unmet.

'Each course of IVF currently costs a couple (or the NHS) from £1000 to £3000, and carries a failure rate of at least 80 %.'

LEGAL FRAMEWORK

Introduction

The Human Fertilisation and Embryology Act 1990 came about largely as a result of the findings of the 1984 Warnock Committee report which was commissioned by the Government following the birth of the first test tube (IVF) baby in 1978. Prior to the passing of the Act, the Royal College of Obstetricians and Gynaecologists operated a voluntary system of regulation.

Parliament decided that embryo research and donation of gametes is acceptable practice only if subject to strict controls. The Act makes provisions to regulate and monitor treatment centres and to restrict research using human embryos, by means of a licensing system. The Act prohibits certain activities and creates a number of criminal offences.

The licensing system in the UK is the most comprehensive anywhere in the world. Some countries have no regulatory system at all; others have limited controls. Within the EC, matters of medical ethics are primarily for member States, and the European Commission, while encouraging co-operation between member states, has said that it does not intend to interfere with the domestic legislation of member states in the field of IVF and infertility treatment.

'Parliament decided that embryo research and donation of gametes is acceptable practice only if subject to strict controls.'

The Human Fertilisation and Embryology Act 1990

Three areas of activity are covered by the Human Fertilisation and Embryology Act:

- fertility treatment which involves the use of donated eggs sperm (*eg* donor insemination) or of embryos created outside the body (IVF). These are referred to as licensed treatments;
- storage of eggs, sperm and embryos;
- research using human embryos.

Not all fertility treatments need to be carried out at a licensed centre. A licence is not required for assisted conception where the gametes are provided by the couple themselves and IVF is not used, nor for GIFT where the gametes also come from the couple themselves.

The Act provides that no person who has a conscientious objection to participating in any activity governed by the Act is under a duty to do so.

The Act establishes the status of a child born through new reproductive techniques where that is unclear. The woman who carries or has carried a child is regarded as the mother, whatever the genetic origins of the child. The husband whose partner is pregnant or has carried a child, as a result of either GIFT or IVF procedures where his sperm has not been used, is presumed to be the father of the child unless it can be shown that he did not consent to the pregnancy. A sperm donor is not to be treated as the father.

'A sperm donor is not to be treated as the father.'

The Human Fertilisation and Embryology Authority

The 1990 Act established the HFEA as an independent body, funded partly from public funds and partly by licensed centres, to carry out the work laid down by the law. A major function of the HFEA is to inspect and license centres. As well as licensing, it has several other responsibilities, including:

- to publish a Code of Practice giving guidance to centres on how they should carry out licensed activities;
- to keep a confidential register of information about donors, patients and treatments;
- to publicise its role and the services which licensed centres provide;
- to give advice and information to the licensed centres;
- to give information and advice to people seeking fertility treatment, to donors, to people who may need to store their sperm, eggs or embryos for medical reasons, and to the general public;
- to keep the whole field of fertility treatment and research under review, whether the activities are licensed or not, and make recommendations to the Government if asked to do so.

The HFEA has 21 members. They are appointed by the Secretary of State for Health to represent a broad range of views and experience, medical, scientific, social, legal, lay and religious. The HFEA considers licence applications, grant licences where appropriate and decides policy. It is chaired by a lay person and appoints the Chief Executive.

The HFEA has a duty to monitor treatment and research, both in general and at particular centres. It has an ongoing programme of inspection of centres and the power to suspend or revoke a licence if licence conditions are not met satisfactorily.

Information Register

The HFEA must by law keep a register of information about individuals undergoing licensed treatments and about donors. The register was set up on the 1st August 1991 and contains information about children conceived from that date onwards. The HFEA will have a legal duty to tell adults who ask whether they were born as a result of treatment using donated eggs and sperm. People aged 16 and over who ask, will be told whether the

'The HFEA has a duty to monitor treatment and research ... '

register shows they are related to someone they want to marry.

No information about patients, their children, and donors will be given out by the HFEA. The names of the children are not collected. The law does not allow people who apply for information from the register to know the identity of current or past donors, or of patients or their children. Indeed, it is a criminal offence to disclose that information. In future, Parliament may alter the regulations so that adults who contact the HFEA and learn that they were born as a result of treatment using a donor, can also be told some details about the donor. The kind of information the HFEA collects relates to a donor's appearance, interests, and occupation, and this may be disclosed. This information may be of use to children in understanding their genetic origins, but the law forbids the names of current and past donors from being disclosed.

'In future, Parliament may alter the regulations so that adults … can also be told some details about the donor.'

Licensed Centres

The Act itself lays down conditions to which licensed centres must adhere and in addition the HFEA issues a Code of Practice. The Code is concerned not only with securing the safety or efficacy of particular clinical or scientific practices, but also with areas of practice which raise fundamental social and ethical issues. The purpose of the Code of Practice is:

- to give guidance to centres about implementing the Act;
- to raise the standards at all centres to those of the best;
- to provide a framework for good practice.

The Code covers the appropriate qualifications of staff at clinics, what facilities should be available, and emphasises that individuals may only be given licensed fertility treatments, become donors, or have eggs, sperm or embryos stored if they have given consent in writing.

Centres offering treatment must take into account the welfare of any child who may be born as a result of the treatment, including the need of that child for a father, and of any other child who may be affected by the birth. The Code explains that centres must look for indicators of risks to the future well-being of the child, and should bear in mind the commitment of people seeking treatment to having and bringing up a child or children.

People seeking treatment must be given appropriate information and must be offered counselling. The Code describes the sorts of information which should be given, the kind of counselling which should be available and the reasons why it is an important part of the treatment. The Code also says that donors must be offered counselling about the implications of donation.

The Code recommends age limits for all donors (18-35 for women and 18-55 for men). In addition, all donors must be screened for medical disorders, including HIV.

Research

All research on human embryos in the UK must be licensed by the HFEA. Research is allowed to promote advances in the treatment of infertility, to increase knowledge about the causes of miscarriages and genetic disease, and to develop more effective methods of contraception. The HFEA can only grant a licence if it is satisfied that the use of human embryos is essential and some types of research are not permitted at all.

Storage

Sperm and embryos may be frozen and stored but only with the consent of the donors. Maximum storage periods are set by law.

Consents

The Act requires that written consents be obtained from donors and those undergoing treatment, and provides that they may withdraw or vary the terms of a consent. Anyone consenting to the storage of their gametes or the embryos produced from them,

'People seeking treatment must be given appropriate information and must be offered counselling.'

must state what is to be done with them if he or she dies or becomes incapable of varying or revoking the consent. If the intention is to create an embryo outside the body, the donors of the gametes must specify for which one or more of the following the embryo may be used, that is, treatment for themselves, treatment for others, or research.

Enforcement

Licences are issued subject to conditions and the Authority also has power to issue Direction to treatment centres. Payment of donors is regulated by Direction. Any breach of the Act, the Code of Practice, the licence conditions or Directions could result in a licence being suspended or revoked. Where a criminal offence may be involved, the HFEA refers the matter to the public prosecution service.

Consultation

The Authority issues Consultation Papers, the responses to which help the Authority to understand and assess the legal, scientific, social, ethical, and moral issues and implications surrounding an existing or possible future development.

ETHICAL *and* THEOLOGICAL CONSIDERATIONS

A Christian Approach to the Treatment of Infertility

In general, the medical task is the restoration to wholeness in every sphere of human life, whether it be body, mind, spirit, or community. This involves restoration of what disease and dysfunction have taken away or, failing this, palliation of symptoms. It also includes prevention of disease and ill-health, and research in order to refine and improve treatment.

The Christian doctor has a profound reverence for life, made in the image of God. It is the desire to cherish and preserve the divine gift of life that, from the Christian point of view is the ultimate justification of the profession of medicine rather than the desire to relieve pain and suffering. The relief of suffering is part of the essential work of healing compassion; but to give it overriding primacy risks leaving the door open to dangerous sentimentality, and even to active intervention to bring about the ending of life.

From a Christian perspective, we understand the healing task in a double theological context. First, there is the context of providence. Healing is part of God's gracious provision in mitigating the effects of human suffering in a world that has fallen away from God's original, good creation. In Scripture we find disease as an element in the death and decay that are the consequence of our disobedience. In God's judgement on human rebellion, we are sentenced to death, but it is a gracious judgement in that God provides health and healing to enable us to live fruitful lives in which he sows the seeds of repentance and faith. Since the context of sickness lies in God's providential disposition of human affairs, it is naive to believe that Christians have any special right to expect human protection or deliverance from accident, disease, and suffering.

' ... God provides health and healing to enable us to live fruitful lives in which he sows the seeds of repentance and faith.'

The second context is the Christian hope of the resurrection of the dead and the life of the world to come. Just as sickness is a foretaste of death, so healing is a foretaste of the resurrection of the body. This conviction both validates the healing enterprise while also limiting it. We can never absolutise healing or any other expectation we may have in this life. The web of human experience is woven of mercy and judgement. Nevertheless, the Christian doctor has a duty to undertake research with a view to improving human health and well-being. Such research may reasonably

' ... healing is a foretaste of the resurrection of the body.'

include bio-medical studies designed to alleviate infertility and improve the health of future generations.

The Christian's response to the trials and disappointments that are part of life should not merely be one of the acceptance of the inevitable. In time can become a cause for rejoicing in the knowledge that suffering and disappointment help forward the development of spiritual maturity (Romans 5:3-4; James 1:4). Infertility may be an example of that suffering and disappointment which God can turn to good account. At the same time, the Christian also knows that 'nothing is impossible with God' (Luke 1:37), and that in answer to prayer a child may be born to a couple who have given up hope. God is a God of surprises.

We fully recognise the extreme pain and grief which childlessness often causes. We also recognise that many single people suffer through lack of loving compassion, sexual fulfillment, and the sorrow of childlessness. In past generations, couples had to come to terms with infertility and accept it as irremediable. Some found fulfillment in adoption or fostering. Thanks to advances in reproductive medicine, today many infertile couples can be assisted to have their own children, provided the obstacles of cost and availability can be overcome. However, in many cases these obstacles are insuperable. What comfort can we bring to couples who find they will never become parents?

We believe that the Lord's word to the Apostle Paul applies: 'My grace is sufficient for you, for my power is made perfect in weakness' (2 Corinthians 12:9). Paul's problem was, of course, different. Yet he was later able to claim: 'I have learned to be content whatever the circumstances' (Philippians 4:12). Many Christians, who have been unable to have children of their own, have found not only grace to overcome their disappointment, but fulfilment in forms of service that would have been impossible if they were parents.

'Infertility may be an example of that suffering and disappointment which God can turn to good account.'

'… many single people suffer through lack of loving compassion, sexual fulfillment, and the sorrow of childlessness.'

'Many Christians … have found not only grace to overcome their disappointment, but fulfilment in forms of service that would have been impossible if they were parents.'

page 52

The Family and Reproductive Technology

Reproductive technology presents a new challenge to the family as it has been traditionally understood.

According to Scripture, God in Jesus Christ has redeemed and sanctified marriage from its state in the fallen world and restored it to its original character and purpose as taught by Jesus (Matthew 9:4-6; Mark 10:6-9; Genesis 1:26-28; 2:20-24). God has created and redeemed marriage between one man and one woman, which may not be broken without affecting our relationship with God. Christian marriage takes place within, and is sealed by God's covenant relationship with his people (Ephesians 5:21-33; Malachi 2:10f). In marriage, man and woman become one. It accords with this doctrine that only in marriage is procreation to occur. Man and woman share in the privilege of being God's representatives on earth. This privilege extends to procreation. As God created them as images of himself, so they together procreate a being who shares with them the image of God. Eve recognised this after she became pregnant to Adam and gave birth to Cain: 'With the help of the Lord I have brought forth a man' (Genesis 4:1). It is out of the physical and personal togetherness of man and woman that an embryo comes into being.

Reproductive technology, however, has loosened the ties between man, woman, sexuality and reproduction, and has rearranged the ways in which they may relate to one another. The use of gametes from a third party introduces into the sanctity of the marriage union an external factor. Furthermore, procreation may now be separated from sexual intercourse. Reproduction can become non-sexual. A woman can become a mother without ever having been a wife or a partner. Parenthood is now possible for widows, single persons, homosexual and lesbian couples, and menopausal women.

Assisted reproduction techniques have also fragmented the

' … only in marriage is procreation to occur.'

'Reproductive technology … has loosened the ties between man, woman, sexuality and reproduction … '

traditional concept of parenthood. A child may have parents who have never met, or a parent who died years ago before he or she was born. Donor insemination may mean that the carrying mother is not the genetic mother of the child she carries, or that the husband of the mother is not the genetic father. It is now necessary to distinguish between genetic, gestational, and rearing mothers, and between genetic and rearing fathers. Surrogacy similarly introduces a third party outside the marriage into the reproductive process.

In these different ways, the structures of the natural family as created by God have been breached. The clear lines of relationship between the different members of the family have been blurred creating a crisis of identity for both children and parents.

In the case of IVF between husband and wife, the sanctity of the marriage bond has not been breached. Children should be the fruit of their parents' love which is normally expressed in sexual intercourse. But if love-making cannot lead to conception, assisted reproduction, though clinical, can rightly be seen, not as a replacement for sexual intimacy, but as something which brings comfort and joy to loving parents.

The Study Group holds firmly to the biblical understanding of parenthood by a heterosexual couple within the marriage bond as the divine norm, and is opposed to those uses of assisted reproduction which in effect deconstruct the family as created by God.

The Central Question

What respect is due to the human embryo?

The question – 'What respect is due to the human embryo?' – lies at the heart of the debate surrounding reproductive medicine.

What are our moral obligations to the embryo? What moral rights does it possess?

Debate has tended very largely, although not entirely, to highlight biological issues and to draw the logical consequences of the standpoint adopted.

Three viewpoints on the moral status of the embryo have been advocated:

- The embryo has no moral status at all.
- The embryo does have a degree of moral status on the ground of its uniqueness and potential, but our moral obligations to the embryo may be outweighed by other moral demands, such as the duty to help infertile couples, or to reduce the incidence of genetically transmitted diseases.
- The embryo is entitled to protection as a human being from the time of fertilisation onwards.

The embryo has no moral status at all

Support for this view is found in the fact that a high proportion of fertilised embryos do not implant and are aborted. In the light of such prodigal natural wastage we cannot claim that the embryo has a right to life.

To this it can be replied that embryo wastage of itself cannot tell us what the embryo is. Large numbers of people lose their lives as a result of natural occurrences like floods, drought, and earthquakes, but such loss does not tell us anything about the nature of the individuals lost. Nor does the fact that many embryos fail to survive in the natural course of events allow us to conclude that they have no value and may be destroyed.

Appeal is also made to the occurrence of twinning. The argument is that until the primitive streak stage, the embryo can divide into twins, and is therefore not yet established as an individual. Until it is clear that there is either one individual or two clearly distinct individuals, it is meaningless to speak of a person, since how can one person become two persons.

The logic of this argument is questionable. If we are not sure whether one or more persons is present, does that justify us in treating what is before us as if there were no persons present?

Finally it is argued that since the early embryo is an aggregate of cells without even rudimentary human form or the capacity for sentience, it cannot be accorded moral status. Behind this argument is the view that the rights of a conceptus develop gradually as the zygote becomes an embryo and the embryo a fetus, until a certain point is reached when it attains the status of a person, and thus the right to be valued as such. No one can say with any accuracy when such a point is reached, but the development of the nervous system and the capacity for sentience during the second trimester of a pregnancy would be an indicator. Until then, the argument runs, the embryo has no claim to be treated as a person since it is argued that personhood has to do with capacities and functions.

If our humanity, however, is to be understood in the light of the fact that we are created in the image of God, and our uniqueness lies not so much in our capacities and functions but in what we are and are called to be, then the argument falls to the ground. It is what we are and are called to be which determines what we do and not the other way around. The potential for those capacities and functions, without which some argue that we may not speak of a person, is present from conception. The embryo contains within its genetic code all that is needed to become a person. Only its development is necessary. That development is to be seen not as growth into that which it was not before, but rather as the fulfillment of that which it already is. There is therefore continuity of identity from zygote to fetus, from fetus to new-born child, and from new-born child to adult. The use of various criteria to define personhood and establish the point at which an embryo or fetus becomes a person is arbitrary and subjective.

'The embryo contains within its genetic code all that is needed to become a person.'

Some question the argument from potential on the ground that being a potential heir to certain rights is not the same as possessing those rights. For example, the fact that someone is the potential heir to a family fortune does not confer ownership rights in the present.

In answer it may be argued that the embryo has the capacity to become what it potentially is. It is true that it cannot realise that potential on its own. Its development is dependent on it being implanted in its mother's womb. Nevertheless, the embryo is a potential person in that, given the right conditions, it will become not something different, but that which it already is.

The embryo has a degree of moral status

This viewpoint holds that the embryo deserves respect greater than that accorded to other human tissue, but not the respect which is given to actual persons. This view is widely held. It is the position taken by the Warnock Report in 1984, which says: 'The human embryo is not under the present law of the UK accorded the same status as a living child or an adult, nor do we necessarily wish it to be accorded the same status. Nevertheless we were agreed that the embryo of the human species ought to have a special status.' The Report and its conclusions underlay the provisions of the Human Fertilisation and Embryology Act passed by Parliament in 1990, and the work of the Human Fertilisation and Embryology Authority set up by Parliament in 1992 to monitor the working of the Act.

The argument behind this intermediate position is that while the embryo claims respect because it is genetically unique and has potential to become a person, yet it should not be treated as a person because it does not as yet have differentiated organs, much less the developed brain, nervous system, and capacity for sentience that legal subjects ordinarily have. It is not yet an individual since twinning may occur, and in any case may never

'"The human embryo is not under the present law of the UK accorded the same status as a living child or an adult .... Nevertheless we were agreed that the embryo of the human species ought to have a special status."'
(Warnock Report 1984)

realise its human potential. This argument rests primarily on biological issues.

In practice, special respect for the embryo means that research on, or intervention with, an embryo which will be used to start a pregnancy, may only be undertaken with the greatest care since there is an obligation not to harm the person who might be born after implantation in the womb.

The implications of special respect for embryos which are not implanted to the womb is, in practice, less clear. Those who accord to the embryo the same rights as a living person, require that all embryos be implanted and would object to research on spare embryos followed by their destruction. Others, while agreeing that embryos should be transferred whenever possible, would allow research in certain circumstances. Other forms of respect shown to the embryo reflect regard for the personal feelings or religious convictions of those whose gametes have produced the embryo rather than a belief in the rights of the embryo itself.

The question of what respect should be accorded to the embryo, whether total in view of its nature and potential, or limited because that potential has yet to be realised, is raised by the late Professor Donald MacKay. He also raises the issue of natural wastage. In the context of a discussion of Psalm 139, he makes a distinction between those fertilised ova he calls 'Xs', which are spontaneously aborted at 'too early a stage for any of the minimal structures for recognisably personal life (not just human life) to have developed', and those which develop into infants and ultimately adults, which he calls 'Ns'. The writer of Psalm 139, who traces his identity from adulthood back to his conception, is an 'N'. 'But, asks MacKay, 'where, oh where, does Psalm 139 say anything whatever about the "Xs" of this world? .... People seem to be arguing that because in case "N" (where the evidence comes from those who have "made it" as persons) God's concern for their whole world line was personal, therefore in case "X" God must view the fertilised egg as a person (with the rights of a person). I don't know any canon of logic by which this follows! In the case of the "Ns", of course, there is direct continuity of identity. But in the case of the "Xs", on what grounds could it be claimed that there ever was a person with personal identity? .... In the case of the "Xs", then, it seems entirely consistent with the biblical data to take the view that there never has been a person there: that in this case the "person" is only a might-have-been, and not an existent to whom moral obligations are owed". Conversely, in the case of the 'Ns', there comes a stage in their development before which 'there is nobody there, but after which there is someone who is "he" or "she" as a personal cognitive agent, however limited in capacities.'

It can rightly be objected that Mackay's argument is valid only if personhood is defined in terms of capacities or functions. But if the worth of the embryo lies in the fact that it is created in God's image, is genetically complete, and is as much the object of God's concern as the fetus, the child, or the adult, then the distinction he draws between 'Xs' and 'Ns' is perhaps less helpful than at first it might appear. The genetic programme present in the embryo determines the process which one day will be complete in the adult. The different stages of development (*eg* embryo, fetus, new-born child, toddler, *etc*) are part of the same continuum. We do not become fully human when the programme is complete. Our humanity is given from the moment of conception.

It can further be argued that if we feel unable to affirm that every conceptus is a person, Psalm 139 makes clear that in some cases at least there is continuity of identity from conceptus to adult. This view is supported by the medical facts. While it is true that when the fertilised ovum begins to divide it remains a cluster of cells which some would not regard as even a potential human being since half of those cells will form the placenta, it is also true that the other remaining cells are destined to form the new fetus. Given that it is impossible to know which is which, should we not treat all in the light of what we know about some?

'We do not become fully human when the programme is complete. Our humanity is given from the moment of conception.'

The Embryo is Sacrosanct

The third view holds that the rights which we accord to a person belong to a developing embryo from the beginning, and the conceptus therefore is a person, from the point of conception ('before I formed you in the womb, I knew you' – Jeremiah 1:5). This view is both logical and consistent with the belief that human life, which begins at conception, is a gift from God, and that the embryo as it develops in size, structure, and specialisation into a fetus is a potential person made in God's image. Attempts to determine whether or not the embryo at any given stage in its development is a person or manifests God's image, in order that we might know how to behave towards it, can only end in sterile argument.

As we stated earlier, much of the current debate highlights, primarily, but not entirely, biological issues and seeks to draw the logical conclusions from the different attitudes adopted toward the human embryo. However helpful and important this is, our ethical attitude to the human embryo is not based solely on biological issues and the logical conclusions so drawn. Our ethical understanding is determined by our theology.

Theological Perspective

The Miracle Of Human Life

Human life may be thought of as a process. However, it is not simply a biological process and cannot rightly be understood exclusively in biological terms. In a sense, the creation of a new human being starts when a man or a woman are attracted to one another and establish a relationship which ideally will find sexual, emotional, and spiritual fulfillment in marriage. The union between a man and woman which results in sexual intercourse may lead to pregnancy. Out of the loving togetherness of husband and wife, a child is born. The sperm and the egg are living cells. The fertilised egg becomes the embryo, which becomes the fetus, which becomes the new-born child, who may properly be seen as a continuation of the life process. With conception a new life begins, a new creation of God, where each person is of supreme value to God, is created in his image, and is being called into his likeness in Jesus Christ.

It is in that calling to be a person, in relationship to, and in likeness to, Jesus Christ, that each person is different from any other person and from all other forms of creation. A human person is radically different from an animal and as such cannot be understood simply as a biological organism. True humanity is understood not only in self-reference, or in relation to others, but supremely in relationship to Jesus Christ and God's unique calling into personhood in the likeness of Jesus Christ. Christ Jesus is divine human person and each human being is a person only in relationship to him and through his continuing creation and redemption of each one.

When Does Human Life Begin?

Despite natural wastage and the fact that a high proportion of ova do not survive and mature, from a biblical point of view human life begins at conception, at which point the human embryo is genetically complete. The Psalmist traces his identity from adulthood back to his conception (Psalm 139). Jeremiah speaks of the fact that even before he was formed in his mother's womb, God had chosen him to be a prophet (Jeremiah 1:5). If we ask at what point the Word became flesh, the answer is at the point of virginal conception. God became flesh at the moment when the Holy Spirit came upon Mary, and the power of the Most High overshadowed her, and she conceived. Christ's conception affirms, confirms and sanctifies every other conception, in the same way

'With conception a new life begins, a new creation of God, where each person is of supreme value to God, is created in his image … '

'If we ask at what point the Word became flesh, the answer is at the point of virginal conception.'

that his Incarnation, his taking to himself human nature, affirms, confirms and sanctifies our humanity. As Christ from the moment of conception was divine, creating, redeeming, person, so every other human being from the moment of conception, is a person in Christ, called into personal relationship with Christ, and must be so regarded and treated with sanctity.

The Sanctity Of The Human Embryo.

'At every stage of life a human being must be treated as a person, enjoying a unique status and of supreme value to God.'

At every stage of life a human being must be treated as a person, enjoying a unique status and of supreme value to God. No person can rightly be treated as a means to an end. This accords with the Helsinki Declaration of the World Medical Association: 'In research on man, the interests of science and society should never take precedence over considerations related to the well-being of the subject.' If we accord to the human embryo the full rights of a person, then all research on human embryos must be morally wrong.

The Study Group disagree at this point with the 'Report of the Committee of Inquiry into Human Fertilisation and Embryology', chaired by Dame Mary Warnock DBE. According to that Report, the human embryo, although it deserves greater respect than that accorded to other human tissue, should not, particularly in the earlier stages, be given the respect that is given to actual persons. It recommended that up to 14 days research on human embryos should be legitimised. That now is the law in this country. According to the theological and ethical position stated above, the human embryo must be regarded as an actual person, and regarded as a person at all stages of development from the moment of conception. Therefore all treatment of a human embryo which is not for the benefit of that embryo is morally wrong and as such all research on human embryos is morally wrong.

A Conflict of Obligations

In everyday life, however, we are continually faced by a conflict of obligations. As Christians we are met by the challenge of the Gospel and the Kingdom of God. Yet we live in a fallen, sinful world. No matter how much we pray and strive that his Kingdom come, his will be done on earth as it is in heaven, this world does not as yet recognise God's rule. It never will until Jesus comes at the last, finally to cleanse away all evil, and transform all things so that they become his renewed and perfect creation. Meantime, we grapple with the task of relating divine ideal to imperfect reality, and are caught in the tension between affirming those norms which God has revealed in his Word and through Christ, such as the sanctity of human life, and applying them to the exigencies of human need and circumstance.

Theologically, as well as pastorally, it is important to recognise this conflict in order that we might avoid two opposite and dangerous extremes. On the one hand, if we turn a blind eye to the conflict and insist on applying divine norms at all costs without regard for the realities of the situation, then as Christians we shall fail to be practical. Our efforts to promote Christian values in public life will meet with little success, and we shall not be able pastorally to address the needs of other people, or yet our own needs, in a way which we believe Christ would have us do. On the other hand, we may so focus on the practical realities and stress the pastoral obligation to minister to people's needs, that we fail to acknowledge, or seek to weaken, the divine norm. In this case we pander to that way of thinking which determines right and wrong primarily on the basis of what promotes a person's sense of well-being (what Hollinger has called 'the triumph of the therapeutic') and allow pastoral considerations to dictate for us new sets of moral principles. We then would be in danger of replacing biblically determined norms with our pastorally orientated principles, on the dubious grounds that, because the

' ... we grapple with the task of relating divine ideal to imperfect reality ... '

Bible is so culturally conditioned by the times in which it was written, it cannot address the needs of people today.

The tension between ethical norms and human need is at its sharpest in the field of reproductive medicine and surfaced again and again in our deliberations as a Study Group. For some, the desire to uphold the sanctity of life and the rights of the person means being against any experimentation on human embryos which is not for their benefit and would lead to their destruction. For others, the need of childless couples and the potential benefits of embryo research, particularly in the field of genetically transmitted diseases, outweighs the obligation felt for the embryo. They justify experimentation up until the primitive streak stage, as permitted by law, though not afterwards. All share an innate respect for the embryo as created by God, and continually upheld by him through the various stages of its development.

In coming to an assessment of their obligations and responsibilities, Christians differ. Some will out of principle apply the norm without compromise. That is not an easy stand to take in the present moral climate where all values are relative. Nor can it be easy to refuse help in principle when the means to assist are available. Others will encourage solutions which seek to reconcile both the ideals of the norm and the demands of the situation. Further differences will emerge because of the ways in which the divine norm is related to individual cases. Christians will differ in the judgments they make and in the way that they assess their obligations in particular circumstances. Those who seek to reconcile both the ideals of the norm and the practical situation will inevitably live with tension, wondering whether they have allowed principle to be eroded by compassion. In this state of tension Christians, who seek to do what is right, need continually to seek the guidance of God, and also forgiveness for ways in which they fall short of God's norm.

The Study Group recognises that a certain latitude of judgment is to be expected among Christians. Strong convictions lie behind the differing positions adopted. In these circumstances it believes that it is not right to make dogmatic pronouncements, nor yet to burden further the already taxed consciences of those working in the field, or of Christian couples who feel it right to receive infertility treatment. Rather, it recommends that the Church and the medical profession, through the continuing study of the medical, theological and moral issues, through consultation and through prayer, should help one another to discern the will of the Lord in a fallen world where divine ideal and human reality are often hard to hold together.

OTHER CONCERNS

Counselling and Support

The 1990 Act requires that before anyone is given licensed treatment, or consents to the use or storage of embryos, or to the donation or storage of gametes, he or she must be given 'such relevant information as is proper'. The Code of Practice issued by the HFEA describes in detail what kind of information this is. It covers, among other things, the limitations and possible outcomes of the treatment proposed, the possible side effects and risks of the techniques involved, the information which centres must collect and pass on to the HFEA, the legal position on parenthood, and the costs of treatment.

The Act also requires that counselling be offered, but clients and donors need not accept it. There are concerns that patients paying for the cost of infertility treatments are often reluctant to face the additional costs associated with counselling.

The Code of Practice mentions three forms of counselling in the context of infertility treatment. They are:

- Implications counselling.
- Support Counselling.
- Therapeutic counselling.

As a Study Group, we welcome the requirement of the HFEA that counselling be offered and recommend that couples avail themselves of the service. We also affirm the role of the Church in supporting childless couples. In describing the forms of professional counselling laid down in the Authority's Code of Practice, we also draw attention to that pastoral counsel which, as Christians, we may offer to the childless at each step of their quest for a remedy for their childlessness.

Implications Counselling

This form of counselling should not be confused with the imparting of information. When a couple suspect that they may be infertile, they will seek information from their GP, relatives, friends, and various publications, so that they can decide what to do. Those undergoing infertility treatment will be given relevant information by the clinician and nursing staff at each stage, so that they can make informed decisions for themselves.

Implications counselling seeks to provide people with an opportunity to consider carefully the effects their decisions will have on themselves, on their relationship with each other, on their family and their friends, and on any resulting children. It will explore their feelings about infertility, about the possible failure of the treatment, about how often they should try, and about perhaps not being their child's genetic parents. These are not concerns which affect a fertile couple. For them, planning and having a family is generally a matter of rejoicing and confidence in how their family and friends will react. But for couples who need infertility treatment, matters are very different. They may question their motives, the 'rightness' of the treatment, what their families and friends will think, and whether, indeed, they should be told.

The Church's role in many instances will be to encourage childless couples to seek medical help, and to assure them that it is alright for them as Christians to explore the options open to them, that feelings of failure and shame are not appropriate, that secrecy is therefore unnecessary, and that among their fellow Christians they will meet with great sympathy for those who long to have a family and cannot, and rejoicing with those for whom infertility treatment has been successful. Couples should also be encouraged to seek God's guidance through prayer as they consider which steps to take.

Support Counselling

Support Counselling must be offered to those who are feeling anxiety and tension, who are experiencing the roller-coaster effect of plunging from hope to despair and climbing up to hope again, and whose domestic relationship is being affected by the strain and stress of repeated disappointment. Couples in such a vulnerable state are easily hurt by the careless and insensitive remarks of friends, and by the sometimes uncaring attitude of some medical people. They may feel inadequate and isolated, and different from 'normal' families. Support counselling aims to give emotional support at all stages, including follow-up after failed treatment. This must be provided by all licensed clinics. Sometimes support is offered by directing the couple to a support group whose members have themselves undergone similar disappointment.

The Church's role is to be aware of the feelings which people have but may not show. These may be feelings of guilt because they are not content with their lot, or because they are jealous of other mothers. Christian couples in particular may have feelings of being let down by God. They should be encouraged to express rather than suppress these feelings. Wrong thinking about God and his dealings with us should be gently exposed and kindly corrected. Above all, we will offer friendship and not avoidance,

'The Church's role is to be aware of the feelings which people have but may not show.'

'The collapse of
false hopes can be
more hurtful than
childlessness itself.'

sympathy and not pity, robust compassion and not sickly sentiment, the assurance that God is in control of all the circumstances of our lives, and the promise of prayer. But we shall beware of giving easy reassurances that their wishes will be granted. The collapse of false hopes can be more hurtful than childlessness itself. Some will have to be helped to accept that children of their own are not part of God's plan for their lives, and to submit to his will in the knowledge that it is best.

Therapeutic Counselling

When anxiety and tension have developed into severe symptoms, and a couple have become obsessional about having a family and begun to behave in an irrational manner, therapeutic counselling is necessary. It may also be needed to deal with acute feelings of grief and loss following unsuccessful treatment.

Michele Guiness, a Christian Jewess, writes about these feelings in her book, *A Little Kosher Seasoning*. She says that she can quite understand why in Bible times, Eli the priest thought Hannah …

> 'was just another wino, drunk by lunch time. She was hurt so deeply that she couldn't speak, crushed not only by the shame of her wayward reproductive system, but also by the endless pregnant bulges of her arch-rival and fellow wife. Lying prostrate in the temple, she tries to move her mouth, but no intelligible words emerged, just an occasional moan or whimper. In one sense she was beyond praying, in a traditional way at any rate, and I've seen how childlessness and other experiences of profound loss can produce pain of that kind.'

Therapeutic counselling aims to help people work through this desperation, moving on from its crippling effects to a stage where childlessness may be accepted, and life go on more meaningfully.

Sometimes Christians experience added pressures because in stressful circumstances irrational thoughts abetted by bad theology may lead them to conclude that, for example:

- God is punishing me. I must have done something wrong.
- God must think I would make a terrible parent.
- I don't have enough faith. That is why God hasn't answered my prayer.
- I'm a Christian and ought to be able to cope.

Here again the Church should try to remove feelings of false guilt, to correct wrong notions arising out of bad theology, to help couples to face reality and think and act in a reasonable manner. It should also seek to show them that, in God's hands, suffering can be constructive rather than destructive, and that he can use their pain to strengthen them emotionally and spiritually rather than to harm them, and to foster their relationship with each other rather than to weaken or even break it.

Counselling of all kinds must be an enabling process, never giving unasked-for advice, but always helping people to move on to a better understanding of themselves, and where they are. In a Christian context, it should lead to a better understanding of God in both his grace and truth, and of his plan for our lives, and result in a more mature faith.

There remains the question of the tension we have already referred to in an earlier section of the report, between divine ideal and human reality. Will the counselling we offer childless couples always result in the 'triumph of the therapeutic'?

It is surely our duty to affirm those ethical absolutes which are expressions of God's character as it has been revealed to us in Scripture and in Christ. Their demands will not be toned down out of a desire to comfort and encourage. Rather, childless couples should be helped to think through the relevance of these norms to their circumstances. The outcome may be that they conclude that certain forms of infertility treatment are open to them, while others are not, which in fact may mean that for the sake of Christian principle, they must come to terms with childlessness, since there is no right to have a child at any cost. Showing compassion never means encouraging people to fulfill their needs, regardless of ethical questions. But it does mean a willingness to

'... there is no right to have a child at any cost. Showing compassion never means encouraging people to fulfill their needs, regardless of ethical questions.'

befriend and support, to remain non-judgmental, and to refrain from offering pious platitudes. To quote Michele Guiness again:

> 'My old Pop used to say when I was a child, "It's vital to have principles," and he was one of the most highly principled men I ever knew, "but principles must always bend for people. When they don't, a fanatic is born". And how his words echo still in my mind when I am faced with the wealth of imponderable ethical dilemmas the fertile process can spawn. There are no easy answers. The Pharisees, with their meticulous code of practice, tried to provide them, by tying up loose ends. Jesus, raised within that system, challenged their rigidity by submitting everyone to sensitive, individual treatment, not an unbendable rule-book.'

Assisted Reproduction using the Gametes of the Partners

Treatments have brought new hope to infertile couples where fertilisation is not possible due to a blockage in the fallopian tube, some forms of male infertility, and unexplained infertility. Since the first IVF baby, Louise Brown, was born in 1978, over 30,000 babies have been born worldwide as a result of IVF.

Nevertheless, the procedure has been strongly criticised on a number of grounds.

The means by which husband's sperm is obtained (mastur-bation) and the fact that reproduction is achieved without sexual intercourse, present difficulties to those Christians who believe that procreation and love-making should not be separated. It is on this ground that the Roman Catholic Church opposes contraception and almost all forms of assisted reproduction.

- The technique is based on embryo research. It also involves the creation of spare embryos which are then frozen for possible use if further treatments are necessary. If they are not needed, they can be discarded, used for research and then discarded, or donated to another couple. Those who regard the embryo as a potential person, genetically complete from the moment of fertilisation, object to it being treated as a laboratory artifact.

- IVF involves the woman in taking medication to stimulate the ovaries to produce a quantity of eggs. The consequent health risks are not insignificant.
- In addition to the physical risks, there is the emotional cost. Many women find the treatment a lengthy, gruelling, and demeaning experience. As one woman expressed it: 'Each course of treatment takes a major psychological toll'.
- The procedure may result in multiple pregnancies, which poses the question of whether selective abortion should be offered, particularly if one of the fetuses is found to be abnormal.
- The cost is high and the success rate low.

GIFT does not require the generation of spare embryos, is a little less expensive, but otherwise the problems are similar to those of IVF (see page 26).

The Study Group is agreed that in cases of intractable infertility, where other methods of treatment have failed, the potential of IVF to relieve infertility should be recognised and accepted. Nevertheless, aspects of the procedure may cause disquiet. We understand those who oppose IVF root and branch, and respect that position. We also understand the position of those who feel able to accept the end (a baby by IVF), while opposed in principle to the means (embryo research). And we recognise that those working in the field are motivated by compassion for the childless. However, the questions which IVF poses remain, and must be openly and repeatedly expressed, lest the growing availability and routine occurrence of the procedure lead to a matter of fact acceptance of a technique which, while bringing help to the childless, is in tension with divine norms.

' ... in cases of intractable infertility ... the potential of IVF to relieve infertility should be recognised and accepted.'

Assisted Reproduction using the Gametes of Donors

The donation of male or female gametes involves the intrusion of a third party into the marriage. The wife may provide the egg, and a donor the sperm where the husband is infertile; the husband may provide the sperm, and a donor the egg where the wife is unable to provide an egg of her own; or both sperm and egg may be donated where both husband and wife are infertile. Thus the husband may not be the genetic father, or the wife the genetic mother of the child.

It is difficult to square Donor Insemination (DI) with marriage as the unqualified acceptance of husband and wife of each other in the totality of their being, fertile or infertile. It may have the effect of weakening the bond between husband and wife and between parent and child.

Research carried out by Dr A McWhinnie into 54 couples and their children, 23 of which had been treated for infertility by DI and 31 by IVF or GIFT, using their own gametes, shows that the outcome has been better in the IVF group than the DI sample. What to tell their children, when and how, also was proving to be a problem. Most felt that they need not be told, but acknowledged the strain of keeping the truth from them, the wider family, the Church, and the community. There was also the anxiety that their children might inadvertently find out the truth about themselves. The fact of parental silence could prove as hurtful as the discovery of their origins. The present rules of confidentiality are weighted towards the donor, which makes it difficult for parents to give their children any meaningful information.

The affect on children of not knowing who is their genetic father or mother is a cause for concern. Collaborative reproduction obscures lineage and genetic connection. Leon Kass writes: 'Clarity about who your parents are, clarity in the lines of generation, clarity about whose is whose, are indispensable foundations of a sound family life, itself the foundation of civilised community. Clarity about your origins is crucial for self-identity, itself important for self-respect.'

For all these reasons, most of the Study Group were opposed to DI, which is in accord with the present position of the Church of Scotland. Nonetheless, it was recognised that DI is widely practised and that the attitude of society is changing from disapproval to acceptance.

Multiple Pregnancy and Selective Reduction

Contrary to the 'happy family' image in the media of multiple births, the reality is often starkly different. Many surviving infants after multiple birth are extremely immature, and some are likely to be seriously handicapped. Over and above the risks for the babies are the threats to the health of the mother. Furthermore, the financial, social and emotional strains consequent on multiple births can be devastating.

Multiple pregnancies have risen over the years, partly because of the use of fertility drugs to stimulate ovulation, but occasionally because of multiple embryo or egg replacements during IVF or GIFT. To reduce the occurrence of multiple pregnancies, the HFEA's Code of Practice has limited the number of embryos which may be implanted at one time to three.

When a multiple pregnancy occurs, the doctor has to help the couple decide on the best course of action. Many couples will accept the risks and continue with the pregnancy. Others may opt to terminate the entire pregnancy, but for infertile couples who desperately want children, that is an unhappy prospect. A third option is selective reduction of pregnancy which was first used when one twin had a fetal abnormality. The normal twin continued to term.

'Contrary to the "happy family" image in the media of multiple births, the reality is often starkly different.'

The Act brought selective reduction within the orbit of the Abortion Act (1967) as amended. The procedure must be related to one of the grounds for lawful abortion, namely:

- the termination of the pregnancy if necessary to prevent grave permanent injury to the physical or mental health of the pregnant woman;
- the continuance of the pregnancy would involve risk to the life of the pregnant woman, greater than if the pregnancy were terminated;
- there is substantial risk that if the child were born it would suffer from such physical or mental abnormalities as to be seriously handicapped;
- the continuance of the pregnancy would involve risk greater than if the pregnancy were terminated, of injury to the physical or mental health of the pregnant woman or any existing children of her family.

Those who oppose abortion on principle will find selective abortion equally abhorrent. Even many who otherwise support abortion may regard the creation of pregnancy followed by its immediate destruction as exhibiting an unacceptable disrespect for early human life. Perhaps a distinction has to be drawn between deliberately risking the induction of multiple pregnancy with the full intention of using fetal reduction, and resorting to fetal reduction only where high order multiple pregnancy occurs inadvertently.

Follow up is required of the effect of selective reduction on the mother or the surviving children. Initially, the mother may feel relief after selective reduction, but later she may have feelings of guilt or bereavement. Clearly prevention is better than cure, and everything should be done to prevent the dilemma for parents in the first place.

Sex Selection

A question with important ethical considerations is whether or not parents have the right to determine the sex of their own infant.

' ... many who otherwise support abortion may regard the creation of pregnancy followed by its immediate destruction as exhibiting an unacceptable disrespect for early human life.'

This topic is very large in its own right and has been extensively debated.

If readily available, there is little doubt that many couples would avail themselves of the opportunity to determine the sex of their child. There are many reasons why couples might wish this:

- When the couple carry a defective gene which is linked to the sex of the child. For example, haemophilia only affects male children and parents may choose, in those circumstances, only to have female children.
- When there are strong cultural or social pressures for a child of a particular sex. These pressures are particularly strong in some ethnic traditions where there is a desire for male children.
- When family sizes are getting smaller, couples may wish one boy and one girl; the desire to choose the sex of a child may be even stronger in circumstances when there is only a one child family – as, for example, in China.
- Personal preference.

Some of the more important arguments for and against sex selection are the following:

In favour of sex selection:
- The rights of individuals to be free to make their own decisions in such a personal matter should be respected.
- In some societies, the availability of male children (for example to do labouring work) may be essential for family viability and stability.
- The prevention of sex-linked genetic disease.

Against sex selection:
- Sex selection may lead to an imbalance in the number of men and women in a society and cause instability (some believe, that in most societies, the effects would be small and self-correcting; others argue that fewer women would help population control).
- Sex selection encourages sexual discrimination by fostering the notion that one sex may be more valuable than another and is contrary to the concept that all people are equal in the sight of God.
- Sex selection gives parents the power to determine who their children will be. That is not a right they should have. Their duty is to accept what God the creator has given.

Methods of Sex Selection

Sex selection can be achieved at different time points in the reproductive process; the timing of the method used has a strong bearing on its ethical acceptability.

Abortion

In this method, the diagnosis of fetal sex is made either from a sample of the fluid around the baby at amniocentesis (usually at 16 weeks of pregnancy), or from a sample of placental cells by chorion villous sampling (usually at about 7–8 weeks of pregnancy). Termination of pregnancy is then carried out if the fetus is not of the desired sex. (There are reports that, in some societies, infanticide may be carried out on children of the undesired sex; it is, however, difficult to quantify the extent to which such practices are performed.)

Pre-implantation diagnosis

The development of assisted reproduction methods now make it possible to sample the pre-implantation embryo and determine its sex. This would make it possible to place in the mother's womb only those embryos which were of the desired sex. This method has been used in cases of sex-linked inherited disease. Because of the expense of the technology, it is inevitable that the use of this method of sex selection will be very limited in numbers.

Pre-conception sex selection

Many attempts have been made to develop methods which will improve the chances of conceiving a child of the desired sex. It is quite possible that, in the near future, methods will be developed which will achieve this objective in a much more reliable way than has been possible hitherto. If such a method is developed, it is likely to attract substantial public demand.

Views of the Study Group

Sex selection for sex-linked genetic disease

The Study Group draws a clear distinction between sex selection for this purpose against any of the other indications. It has less objection to the option of sex selection in the pre-implantation embryo than to that of later termination. Pre-conception sex selection would be the most desirable option to prevent sex linked genetic disease should the method become available.

Sex selection for personal preference

The Study Group rejects the use of abortion (and infanticide) to achieve the object of sex selection for personal preference. This view is consistent with the Church of Scotland's stated position on abortion. It also rejects the use of pre-implantation diagnosis of sex for personal preference.

Following public consultation, the HFEA has incorporated into its Code of Practice a prohibition of sex selection for social reasons. The Authority considers that in principle sex selection techniques are acceptable for medical reasons in cases where a woman is at risk of having a child with a life-threatening disease.

Surrogacy

Surrogacy is the practice whereby one woman carries a child for another with the intention that the child should be handed over at birth. There are two main forms of surrogacy arrangements:

- genetic surrogacy – the surrogate mother provides both the egg and the womb to the couple who contracts her services. The sperm is provided by the commissioning father, or by a donor.
- gestational surrogacy – the commissioning mother provides the egg and the commissioning father or a donor the sperm, which are then fertilised in vitro, and the resultant embryo implanted in the surrogate mother's womb.

'The Study Group rejects the use of abortion (and infanticide) to achieve the object of sex selection for personal preference.'

When the surrogate mother is paid a fee for her services, it is called commercial surrogacy. But when a family member or close friend offers to carry a child for an infertile woman simply out of kindness, it is called altruistic surrogacy.

A number of things can go wrong with surrogacy, even with altruistic surrogacy. The surrogate mother may fail to honour an undertaking to refrain from taking alcohol or drugs during the pregnancy. Or she might decide, once the baby is born, that she wishes to keep it in spite of her promise to hand it over. Or the commissioning couple may decide that they do not wish to accept the baby if, for instance, it is born with a handicap. Or, if the surrogate is a friend or relative, her continued involvement with the couple may cause tensions in the marriage.

The Surrogacy Arrangements Act (1985) makes it an criminal act for any person, other than the commissioning parents and the surrogate, to take part in making commercial surrogacy arrangements. No payments other than reasonable expenses may be paid to the surrogate mother. An agreement that a child will be handed over by the surrogate mother to the commissioning parents is unenforceable in law. The surrogate mother is the child's legal mother. When one or both of the commissioning parents have provided the gametes, the couple may apply to the court for a parental rights order that they be treated in law as the child's parents. The legal procedures are similar to those in adoption.

The Study Group is aware that the law in the UK is designed to discourage surrogacy without criminalising the families directly involved. It would not want to see the law liberalised. However, the Study Group is opposed to surrogacy for the following reasons:

- it is an intrusion into the marriage relationship and undermines the divinely ordained bond of husband, wife, and child within the family.
- it requires of the surrogate mother a detachment which in other circumstances one would not look for in a mother. A willingness to give up her child, which in an ordinary mother would be seen as a fault, becomes a virtue in a surrogate mother. The physical, psychological

'An agreement that a child will be handed over by the surrogate mother to the commissioning parents is unenforceable in law.'

and spiritual bonding between mother and child which is an important part of pregnancy is denied.

- where surrogacy is a commercial arrangement, the dignity of the child is violated through its becoming an object of barter.

Marital Status and Assisted Reproduction

The question of who should receive infertility treatment arises because the traditional understanding of the family (a husband, a wife, and one or more children) has been challenged by social developments, especially the growing incidence of divorce, and the increasing number of children born to single women. Assisted reproductive technology has also made the notion of parenthood more complex. The debate about the meaning of the family is carried over into the field of reproductive medicine as unmarried heterosexual couples, same sex couples, and single women, request technical assistance in reproduction.

The Study Group is of the unequivocal view that heterosexual marriage is the appropriate context for the rearing of children, and that therefore married couples should be eligible for treatment and be given priority. The same would apply to remarried couples, though if one partner already has children by a previous marriage, they might find that limited resources meant they were ineligible for treatment under the NHS. The Study Group considers that it is normally inappropriate for a woman to receive treatment if she is past child bearing age.

The Study Group, while not equating cohabitation with marriage, does not oppose the offer of infertility treatment to cohabiting couples whose relationship meets the criteria of faithfulness, stability, and the intention of life-long commitment.

It is the clear opinion of the Study Group that assisted reproduction should not be offered to those in same sex relationships, or to single people who wish to have a child by asexual

' ... where surrogacy is a commercial arrangement, the dignity of the child is violated through its becoming an object of barter.'

' ... married couples should be eligible for treatment and be given priority.'

' ... assisted reproduction should not be offered to those in same sex relationships ... '

means. We do not deny the capacity of people of homosexual orientation or single parents to rear children with loving concern, but we believe it is important for children to have role models of both genders. Further, assisted reproduction should only be used to overcome obstacles to pregnancy in a relationship where child-bearing is the natural outcome.

SUMMARY *and* CONCLUSIONS

No definitive response to the issues raised by reproductive medicine is possible since, as the technology develops, so the questions posed also change. The Report, therefore, can only offer at best a snapshot in time of what is a fast moving scene, and, like all pictures, it is necessarily selective in what it shows. The Study Group recognise that the picture the Report presents will evoke different reactions, depending on the perspective of the viewer. Some may find its conclusions too broad; others too narrow. For their part, the members of the Study Group have tried to give due weight to both the positive and the negative aspects of reproductive technology.

In conclusion, the Study Group:

1. Welcomes the dedicated and responsible work of scientists and doctors in the field of reproductive medicine.
2. Welcomes the establishment of the Human Fertilisation and Embryology Authority and the high standards of practice which it maintains in the UK.
3. Welcomes the advances made in the treatment of infertility and the understanding of genetic disease.

4. Affirms the need for continued monitoring of developments in the field of infertility.

5. Affirms the sanctity of the human embryo from conception, and urges that its special nature be recognised in law.

6. Given that the law allows research on human embryos, welcomes the limitation of research to 14 days, and opposes any extension of that limit.

7. Recognises the differences of view which exist on the ethical acceptability of IVF and embryo research.

8. Recognises that IVF treatment may be right for married couples, and, with reservations, for unmarried couples in faithful, stable, lasting relationships, where the gametes used are those of the partners.

9. Opposes donor insemination (DI), and IVF treatment where either the sperm or the egg are donated.

10. Opposes the offer of infertility treatment to those in same sex relationships.

11. Opposes surrogacy.

12. Opposes sex selection, except to prevent sex-linked genetic disease.

13. Encourages the Church to provide a counselling service for childless couples to complement that provided by the infertility clinics.

General Assembly Deliverances 1996

The following deliverances were passed by the 1996 General Assembly of the Church of Scotland:

9.1 Congratulate the Board on the production of the Report on Human Fertilisation and Embryology and commend it to the Church for study, and encourage its wide distribution, in particular to Scottish Health Boards, their ethical Committees, Local Health Councils, and all our Medical Schools;

9.2 Affirm that the justification of the profession of medicine is the promotion of physical, mental, social and spiritual well-being;

9.3 Note in particular the complexity of the subject matter and the continuing monitoring of developments in the field of infertility;

9.4 Affirm the sanctity of the embryo from conception, and urge that its special nature be recognised in law;

9.5 Given that the law allows research on human embryos, welcome the limitation of research to fourteen days, and oppose any extension of that limit;

9.6 Recognise the differences of view which exist on the ethical acceptability of *in vitro fertilisation* (IVF) and embryo research;

9.7 Recognise that the IVF treatment may be right for married couples and, while not equating cohabitation with marriage, for unmarried couples in faithful, stable, lasting relationships, where gametes used are those of the partners;

9.8 Oppose donor insemination and IVF treatment where either the sperm or the egg are donated;

9.9 Oppose the offer of infertility treatment to those in same sex relationships;

9.10 Oppose surrogacy;

9.11 Oppose sex selection, except to prevent sex linked genetic disease;

9.12 Encourage the Church to provide counselling services for childless couples to compliment that provided by infertility clinics.

Amenorrhoea

Absence of menstruation.
Primary amenorrhoea – when menstruation has never occurred.
Secondary amenorrhoea – occurring after previous menstruation.

Assisted conception

Bringing of sperm and oocyte together to achieve fertilisation.

Azoospermia/Aspermia

Absence of sperm production.

Blastocyst

Structure formed by division of the fertilised ovum which implants.

Blastomere

Structure formed by division of the fertilised ovum.

Conceptus

Fertilised egg.

Decidua

Lining cells of the uterus formed by alteration of the endometrium after fertilisation occurs.

Differentiation

Development of the cells of the conceptus into distinct groups to subsequently produce placental and membrane tissues of the embryo.

Donor Insemination (DI)

Inserting sperm from a male donor instead of the male partner into the vagina or cervix.

Ectopic pregnancy

A pregnancy which remains and develops in the fallopian tube rather than implanting in the uterus.

Embryo transfer

Transfer of one or more embryos to the uterus.

Endometriosis	Growth of cells, which resemble the endometrial lining of the uterus in structure and function, in abnormal sites, most commonly the outer surface of the uterus, the tubes and ovaries and which may result in damage causing infertility.
Endometrium	The lining cells of the uterus which grow under the influence of ovarian hormones and are shed as part of the menstrual flow. The endometrium is the site of implantation of the fertilised egg.
Fertilisation	Union of the germ cells of the ovum and the sperm to produce a genetically complete conceptus.
Gamete	The male sperm or the female egg.
Gamete Intra-Fallopian Transfer (GIFT)	Infertility treatment for unexplained infertility where ova and sperm are collected and mixed then immediately inserted into the fallopian Tube.
Gonadotrophins	Follicle Stimulating Hormone (FSH) and Lutenising Hormone (LH) – Hormones produced by the pituitary gland in the brain which act on the ovary to achieve ovulation and ovarian hormone production.
Gonadotrophin Releasing Hormone (Gn RH)	A hormone produced in the brain which stimulates the release of gonadotrophins.
Gonadotrophin Releasing Hormone (Gn RH) Analogues	Drugs with similar structure to Gn RH which are used to mimic Gn RH and block the production of FSH and LH. These drugs are used in infertility treatment.
Implantation	The burrowing of the blastocyst into the endometrium to allow the pregnancy to be maintained in the uterus and obtain nutrition.

Infertility	Failure to achieve a pregnancy within an accepted period of time – not less than one year of regular sexual intercourse. Primary Infertility – When a woman has never been pregnant. Secondary Infertility – When a pregnancy either successful or unsuccessful has occurred in the past.
Intra Cytoplasmic Sperm Injection (ICSI)	Direct insertion of a sperm in the cytoplasm of the egg in treatment of male infertility.
Intra Uterine Insemination (IUI)	Insertion of semen, which has often been pre-treated, to insert the 'normal' sperm into the uterus either in ejaculatory failure or in association with ovarian hyperstimulation to treat unexplained infertility.
In Vitro Fertilisation (IVF)	Fertilisation outwith the body of collected ova by sperm. The fertilised eggs are subsequently inserted into the uterus or fallopian tube. This treatment initially used to overcome blockage of the fallopian tubes and is also used in cases of unexplained infertility and male infertility.
Laparoscopy	An operation in which the abdomen is distended with gas and a telescope inserted to allow inspection of the abdominal and pelvic contents including the uterus, tubes and ovaries. Some operative procedures may also be performed under vision from the telescope.
Male Factor	This term covers any reason why the male partner's sperm may be less effective or incapable of fertilisation, ranging from a failed reversal of a vasectomy to the absence of viable sperm.
Oligomenorrhoea	Infrequent occurrence of menstruation.
Oligospermia	Reduction in the number of sperm produced.

Oocyte/Ovum	The egg released from the ovary.
Oocyte Donation	The giving of eggs by healthy donors, usually after hormonal therapy has resulted in maturation of several eggs, to be fertilised and subsequently implanted in infertile women.
Ovarian failure	The inability of the ovary to produce eggs. This may be primary ovarian failure when the ovary has never had the ability to produce eggs or secondary ovarian failure when all the eggs have been used at the menopause.
Partial Zona Dissection (PZD)	The process of 'drilling' through the zona pellucida of the ovum to facilitate entry and fertilisation of the sperm.
Pre-implantation diagnosis	The use of tests on the blastmere to identify the presence of inherited diseases or the likelihood of being affected by sex related diseases by sex determination.
Primitive streak	The tissue which is formed by differentiation of the conceptus on about the fourteenth day which will develop into the fetus.

Appendix 2:
COMPOSITION of STUDY GROUP

The Study Group comprised:

Rev. David Easton (Convener), Parish Minister.
Rev. Malcolm Cuthbertson, Parish Minister.
Rev. Donald Inglis, Parish Minister.
Rev. Ramsay Shields, Parish Minister.
Rev. David Torrance, retired Parish Minister.
Mrs Ann Nelson, Solicitor.

Mrs Christine Paterson, member of the Board, Church Elder.

Mrs Maureen Stitt, Vice-Convener of the Board.

Mrs Renee Taylor, retired Teacher, Member of the Board.

Mrs Marjorie Walker, retired Social Worker.

Professor David Short, Professor Emeritus of Clinical Medicine, University of Aberdeen; former Chairman of the University and Grampian Health Board Committee on Medical Ethics; Physician to the Queen in Scotland.

Dr Garrick Osbourne, Consultant Obstetrician and Gynaecologist, Bellshill Maternity Hospital.

Professor Peter Howie, Professor of Obstetrics and Gynaecology, University of Dundee.

Dr Stephen Lunn, Senior Scientific Officer, MRC Reproductive Biology Unit, Edinburgh.

Dr William Hossack, General Practitioner.

Dr Rae Mealyea, General Practitioner.

Rev. Robert Rae, Hospital Chaplain, Ninewells Hospital, Dundee.

Appendix 3:
ACKNOWLEDGEMENTS

Dr Alexina McWhinnie, Senior Research Fellow, University of Dundee.

Mrs Flora Goldhill, Chief Executive, Human Fertilisation and Embryology Authority, London.

Joyce MacIntyre, Director, Society for the Advancement of Brain-Injured Children.

Rev. Dr E David Cook, Director of the Whiteford Institute, Oxford.

The Most Rev. Richard Holloway, Bishop of Edinburgh, Primus of Scotland.

Professor Stephen Hillier, Professor of Reproductive Medicine, Department of Obstetrics and Gynaecology, University of Edinburgh; member of the HFEA Committee.

Professor Marianna Gensabella Furnari, Professor of Moral Philosophy, University of Messina, Italy.

Professor Peter Brand, Emeritus Professor of Italian, University of Edinburgh.

Angela Lumsdon, Political Relations Manager, The National Infertility Awareness Campaign.

Scottish Health Boards for the provision of data in relation to assisted conception.

Appendix 4:
SELECTED BIBLIOGRAPHY

'Acting or Letting Go: Medical Decision Making in Neonatology in the Netherlands': E Van Leeuwen and G K Kimsma, *Cambridge Quarterly of Healthcare Ethics* 2, 265-269 (Cambridge University Press, 1993).

'Artificial Insemination by Donor': Report of Committee on Temperance (1960), *Deliverances* 11, 12, p 432.

'Artificial Reproduction. Report on a consultation and research findings': World Health Organisation, Copenhagen (28-29 March 1985), *Human Reproduction* (1987) 2. pp 169-172.

'Assisted Conception – current techniques and prognosis': Hull, *Current Obstetrics and Gynaecology* (1994), 4. 122-128.

'Assisted reproduction': R Shaw, *Current Obstetrics and Gynaecology* (1994) 4. 121.

'Assisted reproduction: a not so bright future?': Benagiano and Rowe (1995) *Human Reproduction* 10. 6: 1324-1326.

'Assisted Reproduction and the Male': Irvine, *Current Obstetrics an Gynaecology* (1994) 4. 129-136.

'A study of parenting of IVF and DI children': Dr A McWhinnie, paper delivered to 10th World Congress on Medical Law, Jerusalem, August 1994, published in *Medicine and Law*.

'Bioethics and the Future of Medicine': Kilner, Cameron and Schiedermayer (Wm B Eerdmans & Co, 1995).

'Bioethics in Europe': Rogers and de Bousigon (Council of Europe Press, 1995).

'Childlessness': Board Report to General Assembly of the Church of Scotland (1982).

'Choices in Childlessness': The Report of a Working Party of The Free Church Federal Council and The British Council of Churches (March 1982).

'Comment: A Family Year?': Sutton, *Ethics and Medicine* (1994) 10. 3.

'Contraception': Report of the Committee on Social Responsibility (1976), p 303, *Deliverances* 11, p. 26.

'Council of Europe Parliamentary Assembly Joint Hearing of the Committee on Social and Health Questions, the Legal Affairs Committee, and the Committee on Science and Technology. New techniques in the field of human fertilisation and embryology': Petterson, Elmquist, Warnock and Questiaux, *Human Reproduction* (1986) 1, pp 271-276.

'Council of Europe Parliamentary Assembly Recommendation 1046 (1986) (1) on the use of human embryos and fetuses for diagnostic, therapeutic, scientific, industrial and commercial purposes': Haase, *Human Reproduction* (1987) 2, pp 67-75.

'Creating children: the medical and social dilemmas of assisted reproduction': from *Early Child Development and Care* (1992), vol 81, pp 39-54.

'Current attitudes towards egg donation among men and women': Kazem, Thompson, Hamilton and Templeton, *Human Reproduction* (1995), vol 10, no 6, 1543-1548, 1995.

'Debate: Prenatal diagnosis today': More (*et al*), *Human Reproduction* (1995), vol 10, no 4, pp 765-769.

'Discussion on biological and genetic identity': Kjessler, Parisi and Walinder, *Human Reproduction* (1989) 4, pp 102-107.

'Discussion on ethical and judicial aspects of embryo research': Edwards, Plachot, Renard, Questiaux and Testart, *Human Reproduction* (1989) 4, pp 206-217.

'Donor anonymity and donation between family members': Franco, *Human Reproduction* (1995) 10. 6: 1333.

'Don't ban fetal egg research': Phyllida Brown, *New Scientist* (18 June, 1994).

'Donum Vitae – Instruction on Respect for Human Life in its Origin and on the Dignity of Procreation': Ratzinger and Bovone (1995), Catholic Truth Society.

'Draft Convention for the Protection of Human Rights and the Dignity of the Human Being with regard to the application of Biology and Medicine: Bioethics Convention, and explanatory report': Directorate of Legal Affairs (Strasbourg, July 1994).

'Effects of manipulations in vitro of human oocytes and embryos on the birthweight of resultant babies': Tarin and Cano, *Human Reproduction* (1995) 10. 6: 1322-1324.

'Egg Donation should be limited to Women below 60 years of age': Mori, *Journal of Assisted Reproduction and Genetics* (1995), vol 12, no 4.

'Embryos and Ethics': Cameron (ed) (Rutherford House Books, 1987).

'Embryo Research: Yes or No?': Braude and Johnson, *British Medical Journal* (1989), vol 299, pp 1349-1351.

'Ethics Committees Chapter 14': Warnock, citation unknown, pp 761-777.

'Evangelium Vitae': Pope John Paul II (25 March 1995), Catholic Truth Society.

'HFEA Annual Reports' (July 1994 and July 1995).

'HFEA Code of Practice' (June 1993).

'HFEA Donated Ovarian Tissue in Embryo Research and Assisted Conception Public Consultation Document' (January 1994).

'HFEA Donated Ovarian Tissue in Embryo Research and Assisted Conception' Report (July 1994).

'HFEA Public Consultation Document on Ovarian Tissue in Embryo Research and Assisted Conception.'

'HFEA Sex Selection – Public Consultation Document' (January 1993).

'HFEA The Publication of Centres' Success Rates for In Vitro Fertilisation and Donor Insemination Consultation Document' (January 1995).

'Human Embryo Research – Yes or No?': published by the Ciba Foundation (1986).

'Human Fertilisation and Embryology': The Response of the Board for Social Responsibility of the General Synod of the Church of England to the DHSS Report of the Committee of Inquiry, Board of Social Responsibility (1984).

'Human Fertilisation and Embryology': Board Report to General Assembly of the Church of Scotland (1985).

'Human Fertilisation and Embryology: a framework for legislation': prepared by the Department of Health and Social Security for presentation to Parliament, Cm 259 (1987).

'Human Fertilisation and Embryology – a Jewish view': Chief Rabbi Jakobovits, Office of the Chief Rabbi (London, 1984).

'Human Genetics – a Christian Perspective': Church of Scotland Board of Social Responsibility Report to the General Assembly of the Church of Scotland (May 1995).

'Human IVF, embryo research, fetal tissue for research and treatment, and abortion: International Information': Gunning, Department of Health (HMSO, 1990).

'Human Life and Human Worth': Jackson (1970).

'Human Tissue Ethical and Legal Issues': Nuffield Council on Bioethics (April 1995).

'Human Transplants': Board of Social Responsibility Report to General Assembly (May 1990).

'I sentieri della liberta': Gensabella Furnari, *Guerini Scientifica* (1994).

'In Vitro Fertilisation and Assisted Reproduction': Aburumieh (*et al*) (eds), IX th World Congress, Wien (3-7 April 1995), *Monduzzi Editore*, International Proceedings Division.

'In Vitro Fertilisation: Morality and Public Policy': Catholic Bishops' Joint Committee on Bio-Ethical Issues (1985).

'In Vitro Fertilisation: the ethics': Dunstan, *Human Reproduction* (1986) 1. 41-44.

'Infanticide and the Vulnerable Newborn: The Dutch Debate': Kimsma, *Special Section: From Cells to Selves: Ethics at the Beginning of Life* (1993), p 259.

'Infertility, assisted reproduction and public health': Kaminski and Garel, *Human Reproduction* (1995) 10. 6: 1328-1329.

'Infertility – Epidemiology, Aetiology and Effective Management': Templeton, Health Bulletin 53 (5) (September 1995).

'Is infertility an illness?': Elliston and Britton, *NLJ Practitioner* (11 November 1994), pp 1552-1553.

'Is the Human Person a Substance or a Property-thing?': Moreland and Mitchell, *Ethics and Medicine* (1995) 11. 3.

'IVF Research in the UK. A report on research licensed by the Interim Licensing Authority (ILA) for human in vitro fertilisation and embryology (1985-1989)': Donaldson, Sumfield and Day (Eastbourne).

'Legal and ethics dilemmas of fetal sex identification and gender selection': Morgan, *Legal and Ethics dilemmas*.

'Legislation on Human Infertility Services and Embryo Research': A Consultation paper prepared by the Department of Health and Social Security for presentation to Parliament, Cm 46 (1986).

'Manipulating Life': Church and Society World Council of Churches (Geneva, 1982).

'National Survey of NHS Funding of Infertility Services': Report of Third Survey, prepared by the College of Health for the National Infertility Awareness Campaign (1995).

'Oocyte donation': Abdalla, *Current Obstetrics and Gynaecology* (1994) 4. 137-142.

'Oocyte donation by a daughter': Sureau and Shenfield, *Human Reproduction* (1995) 10. 6: 1334.

'Oocyte donation by a minor to her mother': Schenker, *Human Reproduction* (1995) 10. 6: 1332.

'Our Future Inheritance: Choice or Chance?': Jones and Bodmer (Oxford University Press, 1974).

'Outcomes for families created by assisted conception programmes', reprinted from the proceedings of the IXth World Congress on IVF and Assisted Reproduction held in Wien from 3-7 April 1995.

'Paternal contribution to successful embryogenesis': Menezo and Dale, *Human Reproduction* (1995) 10. 6: 1326-1328.

'Perspectives in Human Reproduction': Hodgen, *Human Reproduction* (1988) 3. 573-576.

'Potential health problems stemming from assisted reproduction programmes': Seamark and Robinson, *Human Reproduction* (1995), vol 10. no 6: 1321-1329.

'Promotion of research in human reproduction: global needs and perspectives': Fathalla, *Human Reproduction* (1988) 3. 7-10.

'Recent deliberations on the case of human fetal oocytes and on pregnancies in post-menopausal women by the British Human Fertilisation and Embryology Authority' (July 1994): *Human Reproduction* (1995), vol 9. no 12. 239-244.

'Report of the Committee of Inquiry into Human Fertilisation and Embryology': Dame Mary Warnock (chair) DHSS, Cmnd 9314 (HMSO, 1984).

'Reproductive Technology and the Law of Canada': Knoppers, *Human Reproduction* (1986) 1. 259-261.

'Response to the Human Fertilisation and Embryology Authority's Consultation Document on Research and Fertility Treatment using Human Ova and

Ovarian Tissue obtained from live Women, Cadavers or Fetuses': Centre for Bioethics and Public Policy, *Ethics and Medicine* (1995) 11. 2.

'Responses': *Human Reproduction* 10. 6: 1334-1337.

'Responses to nine questions concerning research on human embryos': Cohen and Edwards, *Human Reproduction* (1986) 1. 263-269.

'Section 30 – The Acceptable Face of Surrogacy?': Blyth (1993), *Journal of Social Welfare and Family Law*, pp 248-260.

'Selective reduction in multiple pregnancy': P Howie (1988), *British Medical Journal*, vol 297.

'Sex Selection – Ethical Issues': Lilford, *Human Reproduction* (1995), vol 10. no 4, 762-764.

'Society must decide about prenatal diagnosis': Schafer, Arnnemann, Brude and Baumann, *Human Reproduction* (1995) 10. 6: 768-769.

'Some theological perspectives on the human embryo': Atkinson, *Ethics and Medicine* (1986) 2.1 (part 1), 2.2 (part 2).

'Test-Tube Babies – a Christian view': Donald, Scott (*et al*) (Unity Press, Becket Publications, 1984).

'Test-Tube Babies': T F Torrance (Scottish Academic Press, 1984).

'Test-Tube Babies and Embryo Research – Medical and Scientific Perspectives': Sims, CARE Booklet (1988) 3.

'The bioethics of human fetal tissue research and therapy: Moral decision making of professionals': Cefalo, Berghmans and Hall (1993), *American Journal of Obstetrics and Gynaecology* (1994), vol 170, no 1, part 1.

'The case of a sixteen year old donor': Pierce (*et al*), *Human Reproduction* (1995) 10. 6: 1330-1332.

'The child and/or the embryo. To whom does it belong?': Gelier, *Human Reproduction* (1986) 1. 561-652.

'The current ethical controversy over reproductive medicine: prenatal diagnosis': Mori, Brambati and Tutui, *Human Reproduction* (1995), vol 10, no 4, 765-767.

'The current status of preimplantation diagnosis': Harper and Handyside, *Current Obstetrics and Gynaecology* (1994) 4. 143-149.

'The epidemiology of infertility in Aberdeen': Templeton, Fraser and Thompson, *British Medical Journal* (1990) 301, pp 148-152.

'The First Fourteen Days': BBC 'Horizon' transcript of the programme transmitted on 26 February 1990.

'The Human Fertilisation and Embryology Act 1990': article in *The Scots Law Times* (1991), pp 65-71.

'The Human Menopausal Gonadotropin (hMG) Dose in In Vitro Fertilisation: What is the Optimal Dose?, *Journal of Assisted Reproduction and Genetics* (1995), vol 12., no 4.

'The Issue of Sex Selection in Turkey': Kalaca and Akin, *Human Reproduction* (1995), vol 10, no 7, 1631-1632.

'The Management of Infertility and Childlessness': Mason and McCall Smith in 'Law and Medical Ethics'.

'The new gene technology and the difference between getting rid of illness and altering people': Sutton Fil Kand, *European Journal of Genetics in Society*, vol 1. no 1 (1995).

'The Question of In Vitro Fertilization: Studies in Medicine, Law and Ethics': Lejeune, Ramsey and Wright (The SPUC Education Trust, 1984).

'The roles of the individual and organisations in the ethical decision-making process': Edwards, *Human Reproduction* (1988), 3. 11-19.

'The Status of the Embryo from the Christian Point of View': Folscheid, *Ethics and Medicine* (1994) 10. 3.

'The Story of Laurens': Cor Spreeuwenberg, *Cambridge Quarterly of Healthcare* (Cambridge University Press, 1993) 2. 261-263.

'The UK Human Fertilisation and Embryology Act 1990 – how well is it functioning?': Lieberman, Matson and Hamer, *Human Reproduction* (1994) 9. 1779-1782.

'The Upper Age Limit for Egg Donation Recipients': Saunders and Bowman, Journal of Assisted Reproduction and Genetics (1995), vol 12, no 4.

'The Use of Fetuses and Fetal Material for Research': Peel Advisory Group (HMSO, 1972).

'Upholding Human Dignity: Ethical Alternatives to Human Embryo Research': Chargaff, Lejeune and McLean, The Parliamentary Medical and Scientific Advisory Committee to the All-Party Parliamentary Pro-Life Group (1987).

'USA: Politics of fetal tissue research': Siegler, *Lancet* (1992) 339. 1404-1405.

'US public policy on embryo research: two steps forward, one large step back': Fletcher, *Human Reproduction* (1995), vol 10, no 7, 1875-1878.

'Western eyes on China's eugenics law': *Lancet*, vol 346, no 8968.

'What rules for procreation?': Judge Christian Byk, Secretary General International Association of Law, Ethics and Science (1995), *European Journal of Genetics in Society*, vol 1, no 1.

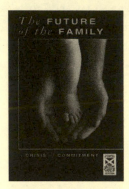

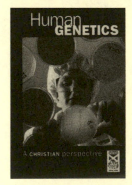
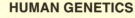

Marriage PLUS
A Study Pack for Couples
A pack for couples about to get married, or for use by those leading marriage preparation classes.
£4.00

HIV/AIDS
Resource Pack
A helpful pack divided into sections, including worship, bible readings and a contact list.
£4.00

Young People and the Media
Study Pack
An ideal discussion starter split into six main sections, with relevant questions and bible readings.
£2.50

Board Information Pack
A pack of 32 cards which give a general introduction on how the Board of Social Responsibility operates, and the range of work it carries out across Scotland.
£1.00

The packs above are available direct from
The CHURCH of SCOTLAND BOARD of SOCIAL RESPONSIBILITY
Charis House, 47 Milton Road East, Edinburgh EH15 2SR.
(Add £1.00 p&p for each item ordered. Cheques payable to 'Board of Social Responsibility'.)

The CHURCH of SCOTLAND BOARD of SOCIAL RESPONSIBILITY

Thank you for buying this book. We hope you found it helpful. If you would like to comment on its contents please write to our Public Relations Officer, Hugh Brown, at Charis House (address below).

The Church of Scotland Board of Social Responsibility is one of the largest providers of social care in Scotland. It employs around 1600 people in 90 homes, units and projects across Scotland from Shetland to Dumfries. It cares for over 4000 people in need every day of the year. Although the staff have a Christian commitment, the Board's services are offered to those of all faiths or none. Our Mission Statement is:

> *'In Christ's name we seek to retain and regain the highest quality of life which each individual is capable of experiencing at any given time.'*

As well as being the Church of Scotland's social work department, the Board also guides the Church on social, moral and ethical issues affecting society. The books and packs mentioned on the previous pages have been produced after relevant reports were accepted by the General Assembly of the Church of Scotland.

The Board relies on funding from a number of sources to continue its work in Scotland with people who need care, support and help. An important contribution comes from donations, gift aid and legacies. If you would like to become a supporter of the Board, or perhaps find out more about contributing financially, please contact our Fundraising Officer, Maurice Houston, at Charis House.

The CHURCH of SCOTLAND
BOARD of SOCIAL RESPONSIBILITY
Charis House
47 Milton Road East
Edinburgh EH15 2SR

Telephone: **0131 657 2000**
Fax: **0131 657 5000**